Steamboatin' Days

A Souvenir of Yesterday on the River.

Mary Wheeler
Paducah, Kentucky

Steamboatin' Days

Folk Songs of the River Packet Era

MARY WHEELER

Louisiana State University Press
Baton Rouge, Louisiana
1944

DEDICATION

To the Courageous Pioneers and Boatmen

Who Made the Rivers a Course of Empire

and

To the Humble Minstrels

Whose Songs Have Preserved for Us Something of

An Era That Is Gone

Acknowledgments

I AM UNABLE to express adequately my appreciation for all the assistance I have received in assembling this material. The pleasant task could never have been accomplished without the kindness of many friends, new and old, who graciously gave me much information.

I wish to acknowledge my obligation and indebtedness to the late Captain Saunders Fowler of Paducah, Kentucky, and the late Captain J. S. Hacker of Cairo, Illinois, for invaluable aid. Captain Sam Smith of the *Waterways Journal* replied patiently to many letters and made it possible for me to record in this volume many facts about the old boats that otherwise would not have been included. For other information on boats and the river I wish to thank Joe Curtiss, Captain J. R. Massengale, Captain Thomas Rees, and Captain Frederick Way, Jr.

My especial appreciation is given to W. L. Beasley, Jr., of Paducah, Kentucky, for the illustrations that were obtained through his generosity and skill. Others who contributed pictures are Mary Elizabeth Edwards, Captain Fowler, Captain W. H. Leyhe, Captain Smith, T. W. Threlkeld, and Captain Way. Two of the river views are from the studio of Caufield and Shook, Inc., of Louisville, Kentucky.

For her very helpful criticisms I am grateful to Mildred Eakes of the Cincinnati Conservatory; for reading the manuscript I am indebted to Dr. Everett Derryberry; and to Mrs. E. W. Jackson I owe much for her friendly help on many interesting trips in search of material.

In addition, my sincere thanks go to Gordon W. Cooper, Captain W. H. Dukes, George Dyke, Captain Sam Felts, Mattie Fowler, Mrs.

Miles Haman, Guy Holland, Captain J. Sam Jackson, Captain Edgar Jeffords, Captain S. R. Lee, Mrs. Roy McKinney, H. L. Richardson, J. N. Twitchell, Captain Frank Wagner, Mrs. Lloyd Emery, Captain Donald T. Wright, and to others not mentioned here.

MARY WHEELER

Paducah, Kentucky

Preface

FOLK SONGS more nearly reveal the heart and soul of a people than does any other form of expression. One of the great periods of this nation's development is associated with the river packet era. Traffic on the waterways reached its peak during this colorful age, and around the great boats a whole body of folklore was created, both in song and story. Much has been written about the importance in history and commerce of the Mississippi and its tributaries; but the songs of the rivers have never been fully recorded and, evanescent as they are, they could too easily be lost.

In this volume an effort has been made to preserve the music of the packet boat era while it is still possible to obtain it. The words and melodies of the songs were taken down from the singing of old Negroes who in their youth worked on the boats.

The search for songs of the packet boat days leads away from broad city streets. Many of the old Negroes live in cabins along the river bank, or on a hill with the broad stream below. Some have found homes in towns on narrow unpaved streets or at the end of an alley. Frequently, the trail winds to a cottage on a country road far off the highway. These old Negroes love to talk about the days when they were "on the rivuh."

The time I like best for visiting with them is during the long summer afternoons. When I find them sitting on their porches or perhaps under a tree near the doorstep, I never feel like an intruder, and even the sight of my notebook and pencil does not spoil my welcome. They do not understand my interest in "steamboat songs" and are puzzled at my insistence that they try to remember half-forgotten lines and tunes.

Usually they watch me without a great deal of amazement as I take down the words of a song, but when I write out the melody they are plainly mystified. The notating of music they speak of as "composin'." Until a song is actually written down or printed, they will tell you that it is "not composed," no matter how many times they have sung it.

Although most of the songs in this collection were found in towns and villages along the southern bank of the Ohio River, many of them tell a story of boats known on the Mississippi and the Tennessee as well. In the packet boat days, wherever great rivers met there grew up important centers for taking on passengers and freight. To these busy wharves and levees the "rousters" would bring songs gathered all along the river highways. They sang of certain great boats, of the rivalry between them, and of the tragedies known only to the river and the sea.

At Paducah, Kentucky, where the Tennessee flows into the Ohio, and at Cairo, Illinois, where the Ohio joins the Mississippi, we can still hear songs and fragments that tell of the beauties of "the ole Tennessee" and of journeys "down below" to the cotton country of the lower Mississippi. Many boats made regular trips between Ohio River ports and destinations on the Tennessee or Mississippi, and the "rouster songs" were heard wherever the Negroes were "steamboatin'."

When I began this study my plan was to collect the words and melodies of the songs, and nothing more. But I soon realized that without some knowledge of the river and river boats the words of many of the songs would have little meaning. This prompted me to include in the collection some facts that were originally intended to be brief informational notes. I have included also some of the strange things the old Negroes told me during my many friendly visits among them—the background and thoughts of the folk singer are so inseparably associated with the song itself.

Contents

ACKNOWLEDGMENTS vii

PREFACE ix

1 INTRODUCTION 1

2 WORK SONGS 10

3 SONGS OF BOATS 39

4 SOUNDINGS 59

5 SPIRITUALS 67

6 SONGS OF MEDITATION 80

7 LOVE SONGS 85

8 DANCE SONGS 92

9 SONGS OF LAWLESSNESS 99

10 APPENDIX 112

INDEX OF SONGS 120

Illustrations

opposite
page

STEAMBOAT BELL 4

"Now Paducah's Layin' Roun' the Ben'" 14

SUNSET ON THE RIVUH 28

FORMER ROUSTER'S GRANDSON 40

PADUCAH RIVER FRONT, 1873 48

STEAMBOAT WHISTLE 56

A MINSTREL OF THE OHIO 68

SUSAN AT THE WELL 76

"COME, LOVE, COME, THE BOAT LIES LOW" 90

THE GENERAL WOOD 104

LIVINGSTON POINT 116

Introduction

NO RIVER has had a more important destiny in the development of America than the Mississippi, and some of the most brilliant and picturesque names in American history are associated with the conquest and occupation of the Mississippi Valley. Through a wilderness minus roads, the powerful Mississippi, with its many tributaries, was a natural avenue of expansion and exploration.

Most important of the Mississippi tributaries was the Ohio, which the Indians called "Oyo" or "River of Many White Caps" and early French explorers named "La Belle Rivière." The first steamboat on the Ohio was the *New Orleans*, built in Pittsburgh in 1811, by the Ohio Steamboat Navigation Company. One of the members of this firm was Nicholas J. Roosevelt, a brother of the grandfather of President Theodore Roosevelt. Under his personal supervision the *New Orleans* was built, and he and Mrs. Roosevelt were the only passengers on the epochmaking maiden voyage. It was predicted and expected by the public that this journey would end in disaster. This boat was built for use in the lower Mississippi, and when she reached Natchez she remained in the Natchez-New Orleans trade. Because the return trip to Pittsburgh was not immediately made, the conservative doubters still maintained that a successful ascending trip was impossible. The channel of the Ohio was, and has remained, dangerous, abounding in bends, snags, and treacherous obstructions. In May, 1815, the steamer *Enterprise* sailed from New Orleans with the announced intention of conquering the ascending currents. To the amazement of thousands she arrived without mishap at Louisville, Kentucky.

The most romantic period of the packet boat was just prior to and following the War Between the States. The packets carried both passengers and "package freight." At this time the railroads were not of great importance, and it was indeed the river's Golden Age. The wealthy leisure class of the South used the river for business and for pleasure, and in the salons and on the decks of the boats of this time a high standard of graceful living and fashion was found.

Between the different boats there was spirited rivalry, not only for luxurious appointments but for speed as well. In some of the old roustabout songs still heard today, we find evidence of pride in what was then considered great fleetness, as in this fragment:

> Rapidan, Rapidan,
> Catch me if you can,
> Shoo fly, shoo.

The "Shoo fly, shoo" signified a contemptuous imitation of the exhaust of the rival boat. In 1815 a little over twenty-five days was required to make the journey from New Orleans to Louisville, a distance of 1,486 miles. Gradual improvements were made in this record.

During the period that the river steamboat was the chief means of transportation and travel, the big rivers were associated with bustling activity and exciting journeys. The wharves were crowded with many boats, Negroes lifting freight, passengers coming and going, and people from the towns who liked to meet the packets for a glimpse of travelers from distant places. The levee stones would ring with the impatient stamping of iron-shod horses, as wagons and drays waited for freight; and there were always carriages for "the white folks."

These proud packets, white and graceful, were palaces afloat. No effort or expense was spared to make them both beautiful and luxurious. Furnishings and equipment were the finest obtainable. Oriental rugs and brilliant crystal chandeliers added to the costly elegance of the salons. In the cabins ample maid service was available at all times; the cuisine was excellent.[1]

Every packet took pride in her whistle and bell. Some of the large bells weighed as much as eight hundred pounds, and great skill went into their workmanship. They were elaborately decorated and were masterpieces of the art of bell founding. This art flourished and attained a high standard, reaching its climax about 1845.

So that the bells would have a clear musical tone, a generous amount of silver was used in casting them. For this purpose silver dollars were melted, as bulk silver was not in us at this time. It was not unusual for a captain, when he desired a bell for his boat, to contribute personally five hundred silver dollars; and, in his enjoyment of the deep mellow

---

[1] The following menu card for dinner served in 1879 on the lower Mississippi packet *J. M. White* was copied from the notes of the late Captain Saunders Fowler:

Soup

Fish: Broiled Red Fish, au maitre d'hotel

| Leg of Mutton, Caper Sauce | Boiled Ham | Corned Beef and Cabbage |
| Chicken, Egg Sauce | | Fulton Market Beef |

| Loin of Beef | Roast Pork | Chicken |
| Saddle of Mutton | | Turkey |

Vegetables

| Mashed Potatoes | Rice | Cabbage | Green Corn |
| Turnips | Snap Beans | | Hominy |

Relishes

Cross and Blackwell's Pickles

Gherkins	Currant Jelly	Cheese	Tomato Catsup
Walnut Catsup	Chow Chow	Piccalilli	Eng. Onions
Mushroom Catsup	Land P Sauce	Olives	Cole Slaw
Maunsel White	Lettuce	John Bull Sauce	
	French Mustard	Horseradish	

Entrees

Calves Feet a la Puceline	Pied de Veau a la Puceline
Fillets of Chicken with Truffles	Fillets de Poulets aux Truffle
Braised Brisket Lamb, green peas	Poitrine d'Agneau au Brazier avec Pois Verts

Game

| Saddle of Venison | Wild Duck with Cranberries |

(Continued on next page)

tone this amount of silver would insure, he would consider the money well spent.

When a boat's business in port was nearly finished the bell sounded slowly quite a number of strokes as a notice to all parties concerned that the boat was about to take her departure. Three strokes of the bell was a signal to the crew on watch to stand by their posts; the engineer replied by blowing three blasts on a small whistle to indicate that everything in his department was in order and that he was ready to leave.

About the time that bell founding reached its height the steam whistle came into use. Which boat was the first to carry a steam whistle is uncertain, but it is said that the packet *Revenue* has a right to this distinction. The *Revenue* was built at Pittsburgh by Captain William H. Fulton. Her first trade was in the upper Ohio.[2] There is a story that

Cold Dishes

Corned Beef   Tongue   Ham Salad

Deserts

White Raisin Pudding   Lemon Pie   Green Apple Pie
Petit Puit d'Amour   Fachennottes, a la Flour d'Orange

Cakes

Pound   Fruit   Almond   Jelly Cake   Lady Fingers
                              Cocoanut Plarine

Creams and Jellies

Jelly de Macedonia   Marisschino Jelly   Belle Fritters
Meringue aux Peche   Creme a la Roman

Fruits

Pecans   Bananas   Apples   Pine Apples
Brazillian Nuts Figs   Almonds   English Walnuts
Oranges   Filberts   Prunes   Raisins
                              Fresh Dates

Coffee and Tea

Wines, see Wine Card at the Bar, Extra Charge

[2] The Ohio above Louisville, Kentucky, is known as the upper Ohio; the lower Ohio is from Louisville to Cairo, Illinois.

Courtesy of Captain W. H. Leyhe

STEAMBOAT BELL

FROM THE PACKET WILL S. HAYES NAMED FOR THE KENTUCKY WRITER. DURING THE FIRST WORLD WAR THIS
BELL WAS SOLD FOR OLD METAL, BRINGING $560.00

Captain Fulton first realized the possibilities of a steam whistle for river boats when he heard a factory whistle blown by steam while he was visiting in the city of Philadelphia, about a hundred years ago.

The steam whistle soon took over some of the duties of communication that had previously been associated with the bell. The great lines evolved their own call, or blast, that was used by all of their boats. This call was sounded in making a landing, but in passing another boat in the channel a universal unchanging code developed. The right of way belonged always to the descending boat, but the ascending craft was the first to announce the direction, either to the right or left, that she deemed best to take in passing. If this was satisfactory to the descending boat, the signal was repeated to signify consent. However, if the descending pilot thought this course unwise, three or more short blasts were given. After this message was acknowledged by a repetition, the descending pilot stated the direction he preferred. Consent of the other boat was again expressed by a repeating of the signal last heard. One whistle blast indicated that the right-hand direction was desired, two blasts the left.

It used to be a point of pride with people who knew and loved the language of the river to be able to recognize the approach of an important boat by the sound of her whistle or bell. Each whistle possessed a tone that could be identified, in addition to its own particular blast, and every great bell had its own individual quality.

In the early days of the steamboat the deck hands were hardy and ambitious young men who desired to study the ways of the river with the idea of becoming pilots, captains, and owners. A little later attempts were made to use foreign labor, especially German and Irish, but without success. In the ante-bellum days groups of slaves were leased out by their masters to work on the Southern boats. No man of any race has been found equal to the Negro for this kind of work. From that time to the present the Negro roustabout has been a type.

When uncultivated people have a feeling for music, we can always find among them a talent for improvising. The Negro, in common with other primitive races, possessed—and still possesses—this gift to a marked degree. The African savage and the Indians had their songs and dances for every occasion of their lives. The Anglo-Saxon bards sang of legends and great events in the life of their race, and our own pioneer ancestors carried their songs with them into the wilderness. The "steamboat nigger" expressed himself in song, as people have always done through the ages. He sang often of the boats that to him took on an almost human personality. His songs deal with the conditions of his life on the river, and they help us, looking back from our own age of rapid travel, to realize the beauty and power of the river at a time when it was not only the "course of empire" but an avenue of romance and adventure as well.

The life of the steamboat rouster was not an easy one. He was on call at all hours for the hardest kind of labor and was often driven by an unmerciful mate to the very limit of his strength. When his back was tired and his shoulders sore, singing relieved his grief.

> They ain't but a thousand mo'—
> My knee bones is achin',
> My shoulder is so'—
> When I make this trip
> Ain't gonna make no mo'.
> Coonjine, nigger, coonjine.

Some of the most vital of the roustabout songs consist of just a few words or a couplet, born from a moment of ecstasy or despair. The loneliness and fatigue that were accepted phases of this hard-working existence are reflected in many of the songs.

> Steamboat nigger ain't got no home,
> He make his livin' on a shoulder bone.

These lines, combined with a refrain that is often a rhythmic jargon, grow almost unconsciously into a song.

Musically, we have in these melodies the characteristics that are generally associated with the songs of the American Negro. Aside from the syncopation that is such a vital and interesting feature of all of the music of this race, perhaps the most striking idiom is the frequent use of the pentatonic scale. Very few of the songs make use of a tone series as extended as our own major and minor scales. The melodies are frequently rhythmic arrangements of three or four tones. We notice a striking absence of half steps.

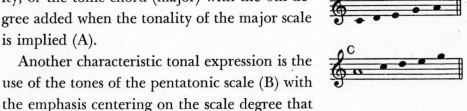

One tone series that is generally used has been described as the pentatonic scale with the 2d omitted when intervals imply that scale tonality, or the tonic chord (major) with the 6th degree added when the tonality of the major scale is implied (A).

Another characteristic tonal expression is the use of the tones of the pentatonic scale (B) with the emphasis centering on the scale degree that corresponds to the minor tonic. This arrangement is classified as the natural minor with the 2d and 6th omitted (C).

We find both major and minor modes, with a more general use of the major. When the minor is used, there is a tendency toward the natural 7th rather than the more familiar melodic and harmonic forms.

The phrases often fall into groups of three, instead of the two and four to which we have become accustomed in many simple song forms. Frequent use is made of the old rondo form, in which the chorus is heard first and last, alternating throughout with the stanzas.

The lines are of varying lengths and accents. The Negroes fit these to the same melody without apparent effort. In this volume the note values are written for the words of the first stanza; in the remaining lines of each song, the ease with which the words and melody are combined produces a chantlike effect suggestive of Plain song.

Following the final double bar of each song I have notated the scale from which the melody is built. The scale numbers given for the pentatonic scale, that is 1-2-3-5-6, are based on the scale degree numbers of the major scale. For convenience, each tune has been written in a key suitable for the average voice, and in the treble clef, in preference to the exclusive use of the bass clef that the singing of the old Negro men would have required, in strict accuracy.

In justice to the material itself, perhaps a word should be said of the difficulties of truthfully notating the melodies. The slides that occur so surprisingly, the quick deviations from an expected pitch, for which the grace note has been used, though inadequately, and the perplexing rhythm that persists so easily, in spite of the demands of the words, all these give the collector a feeling of helpless dissatisfaction with the written record.

As in any group of folk melodies there is some interchange and similarity in both words and tunes. Lines are repeated in slightly different forms in several songs, and often there is a kinship of melodies and no repetition in the lines. From a study and comparison of several variants an entirely new song may emerge that seems in no way related to what might be called the first version. It is often difficult to decide which is the original and which is the variant.

Attempts to classify the material reveal further overlapping. While the majority of songs given in this volume center around boats, many can easily be placed in more than one group. As in all music of the Negro, the greater number of the roustabout songs are associated with labor. As far back as we have any record men and women have lightened their work by singing. With the Negro, as with other people, rhythmic singing eases toil, lightens effort, and refreshes the spirit.

The religious nature of many of the songs did not interfere with their use during the loading and unloading of a packet. Many of them are a sort of chant, with a decided rhythm of the dogtrot type.

Another important group consists of the melodies sung in the evening on the forecastle, often for the pleasure of the passengers on the upper decks. These are less rhythmic and more tuneful than the work songs, but they are equally characteristic. As the steamboat was leaving port, all rousters were required to line up on the lower deck. When the vessel was loosened from the levee a song was "raised." This was always a hymn or spiritual.

These roustabout songs possess more interest for us if we remember their setting—a regal steamboat; passengers traveling in luxury on the upper decks; below, hard labor and toil for "the white folks" without the aid of modern equipment; and through all of them, the background of the river with its power and its force as a part of the fabric of our national life.

2

Work Songs

EXHAUSTING labor was required of the roustabout, and it is not surprising that there is a predominance of work songs in his music.

The hard-driving mate, interested only in getting the freight moved quickly, liked for his men to sing. He would select as leader a Negro who could "raise a song," and then he saw to it that the tune was kept at a fairly rapid pace. The tempo of the singing was an important factor in the length of time required to handle a cargo.

Most of these melodies are in duple measure. They were created as accompaniments to the movements of the body, and the marching or trotting rhythm that developed naturally during busy hours on the levee had a definite effect upon the meter of the songs.

Captain Jim Rees an' the Katie

The first stanza of the song recalls some of the most eloquent chapters of river traditions.

Captain James Rees founded the James Rees Duquesne Engine Works, in Pittsburgh, 1854. Forty years later, the firm was incorporated under the name of James Rees and Sons. This company owned all three of the famous *Kate Adams* boats.

The life and work of Captain James Rees constitute one of the most brilliant achievements of an era when the path of a great river was the chief avenue of commerce. Immediately after the War Between the States, the Southerners had no money to start again in the river trade. Many of them turned for assistance to Captain Rees and obtained from him boats on credit. Captain Rees was willing to accept a promise that he would receive his money later, and it is said that he had no cause, in the end, to regret his generosity.

Rees-built boats have helped to make history on the Ohio, Mississippi, and Missouri rivers, and their tributaries. In addition, this firm has constructed vessels operating on the rivers of Egypt, Russia, South America, and on many other great inland waters of the world.

All three of the *Kate Adams'* belonged to the aristocracy of river craft, and each of them possessed a background of romance and a record for work well done. The first and the second boats of this name had wooden hulls. Much of the machinery and material from the first "Katie" was used for her successor. The third craft had a steel hull.

On March 18, 1885, the second *Kate Adams* made her famous trip on the Mississippi from Helena, Arkansas, to Memphis, a distance of ninety miles. Her time was five hours, eighteen and a half minutes, the shortest time on record between these two points.

The third *Kate Adams,* known among the rousters as the "Lovin' Kate," is the boat referred to in "Captain Jim Rees an' the Katie." The Captain Rees spoken of in the first line is the son of the original founder of the firm. The "Lovin' Kate" was in the Memphis-Arkansas City U. S. Mail trade, and in the latter part of her career she was also a favorite on the upper Ohio, in the Cincinnati to Pittsburgh trade. In 1926 she was leased to the Universal Pictures Corporation for the filming of "Uncle Tom's Cabin." About two months after the picture was completed, the boat caught fire from an unknown cause, at the wharf in Memphis, and burned to the water's edge. There had been a good deal of comment when it became known that the *Kate Adams,* associated with the most cherished traditions of the South, was to be used in filming the story of Uncle Tom. After the boat had burned, the owners, recalling this "levee talk," wondered if the fire could have been of incendiary origin. The first and second *Kate Adams* were also destroyed by fire.

"Captain Jim Rees an' the Katie" can be considered as belonging to the work song group. The melody illustrates the rousters' use of the pentatonic scale. The comfortable swing of the rhythm helps us to visualize the black roustabouts, trotting back and forth "totin' freight."

This song of the "Lovin' Kate" was taken down on a wharf boat from the singing of an old colored watchman and two younger Negroes employed on the levee.

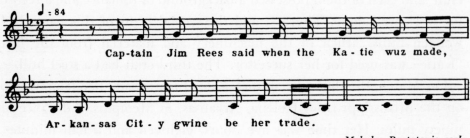

Cap-tain Jim Rees said when the Ka-tie wuz made,

Ar-kan-sas Cit-y gwine be her trade.

Melody: Pentatonic scale.

I lef' my woman in the do',
Says, "Work down the rivuh, an' honey, don't you go."

Captain will you be so good an' kind,
Take all the cotton, an' leave the seed behind.

Heap seed[1] an' a few knows,
Heap starts an' a few goes.

I ain't gwine tell nobody
What they done to me.

But ef I evuh git to the long plank walk,[2]
I won't come no mo'.

[1] Sees.
[2] The stage plank.

I'm Wukin' My Way Back Home

This melody must have been sung first by a rouster who was both weary and homesick. In many of these songs there is a plaint about the heavy work and the hard life, accompanied by a longing for the trip to end.

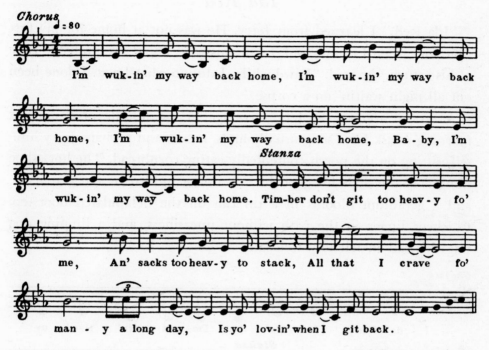

I'm wuk-in' my way back home, I'm wuk-in' my way back home, I'm wuk-in' my way back home, Ba-by, I'm wuk-in' my way back home. Tim-ber don't git too heav-y fo' me, An' sacks too heav-y to stack, All that I crave fo' man-y a long day, Is yo' lov-in' when I git back.

Melody: Pentatonic scale.
Rondo form.

Oh fireman, keep her rollin' fo' me,
Let's make it to Memphis, Tennessee,
Fo' my back is gittin' tired,
An' my shoulder is gittin' sore.

Down in the Mississippi to the Gulf uv Mexico,
Down below Natchez,
But ef the boat keep steppin'
I'll be seein' you soon.

Now Paducah's layin' roun' the ben',
Now Paducah's layin' roun' the ben',
Captain, don't whistle, jes' ring yo' bell,
Fo' my woman'll be standin' right there.

Ida Red

"Ida Red," I learned from Jerry. He was not at home for my first visit, and when I questioned Tessie, his wife, about the probable time of his return, she said, "Lawd, chile, I dunno whar he at. I done been out all night waitin' on a corpse."

A visitor stopping at Jerry's cottage in the middle of a summer morning to ask for a song usually finds Tessie, and perhaps Jerry himself, sitting on the porch contentedly eating cornbread. The horseshoe hung over the door for good luck is almost hidden by the grapevine, and a geranium blooms in a tin can on the delapidated doorstep. Chickens linger in the path without uneasiness, and a limping dog wags his tail in friendly welcome.

Melody: Pentatonic scale—5th omitted.
Rondo form.

Sho' as the grass grows in the fiel',
Got to cook ole John a solid meal.

I'm goin' up town, ain't gwine stay long,
You might as well put on yo' bonnet an' gown.

"NOW PADUCAH'S LAYIN' ROUN' THE BEN'"

Oh, When I Git My New House Done

The *Charleston,* on which "Oh, When I Git My New House Done" was sung, was built for trade in the upper Ohio, but the trip that ended her career was on the Mississippi. On February 6, 1907, she struck a reef at the foot of Wolf's Island near Hickman, Kentucky. The disaster occurred between one and two in the morning.

Attempts were made to save the boat and her heavy cargo of corn, but it was too difficult for aid to reach her because of the ice in the river. Two watchmen were left in charge of the grounded vessel, while everyone else aboard was taken to shore by the towboat *John S. Summers.* The packet stayed on the reef for nearly three days; at the end of that time her cabins and cargo had been carried off or destroyed by the huge blocks of ice and by the merciless current. The *Charleston* had broken in two. Only her whistle and a set of stage blocks were saved. The two watchmen with a goat that was a pet of the crew had made camp on Wolf's Island. They were taken ashore by the *Peters Lee* after enough ice had passed to make river travel less hazardous.

The roustabouts created songs that reflected their thoughts and environment. Often their improvisations included lines woven around the personality of some well-known figure who was loved or feared. The *Charleston* was owned by Captain Frank Wagner, known to his friends on the river as "Captain Cal." From the husky chanting of an old Negro man in Paducah, Kentucky:

> Captain Cal wuz a fine ole man,
> He whupped his wife with a fryin' pan,
> I'm up the rivuh, Lawd, how long will I be gone?
> Oh, Lawd, have mercy on my soul.

When I asked the old Negro if he had ever heard of the *Charleston,* he replied, "Lawdy, chile, I wuz on her when she fust started out."

Oh,   when I git my new house done, I'll will my ole one to

my son. _____   Oh, _____   it's git-tin' so cold

roun' this town, Birds can't hard-ly fly. _____

Melody: Pentatonic scale—2d omitted.

The reason I stayed with the man so long,
He give me something to rare back on,
Oh ——, Lawdy, in the mornin'
We ought to be back home.

Use first half of melody.
Captain, captain, my feet so cold,
Nevuh mind the fire, let my wheelers roll.
Oh ——[3]

Stavin Chain

"Stavin Chain" was taken down from the singing of an old Negro who had been a roustabout on the *Joe Fowler*. The song is well known among the river darkies.

"Stavin Chain" is supposed to have been a real person, a strong and powerful rouster. His personality seems to have gripped the imagination of the Negroes, and he is spoken of as a hero. No basis for this idea could be found.

[3] The words are not just accurate. The "Oh ——" was not used regularly, and some lines were repeated. This is the best version obtainable.

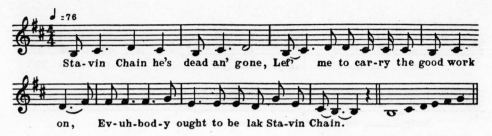

Melody: First six tones of minor scale.
Phrase groups of three.

I'm goin' down the rivuh, goin' to carry a few sacks,
I'll see my woman befo' I git back,
Evuhbody ought to be lak Stavin Chain.

Ashes to ashes an' dust to dust,
Can't hardly tell what woman to trust,
Evuhbody ought to be lak Stavin Chain.

Up Mr. Butcup an' down Mr. Bear,
Looks mighty dirty, but there's a good man there,
Evuhbody ought to be lak Stavin Chain.

Po' Shine

"Po' Shine," like "Stavin Chain," appears often in the songs of the
packet boat days. Uncle[4] Jeff, from whose singing it was recorded, said,
"Yes, Miss, Shine wuz a little black nigger. They thought he wuz
foolish. They called him 'Shine' because he wuz so black. He wuz a
lineman an' they didn't pay him. They took his money because they
thought he wuz foolish."

When Uncle Jeff sings, his voice slides from one note to another in
a sort of wail. He says, "When you moan it, it seem lak it kinda revives
'em, an' pretty soon they all git to hollerin'."

[4]"Uncle" and "Aunt" are titles of affection given to old Negroes by their "white folks."

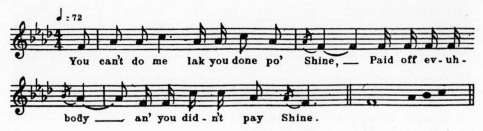

You can't do me   lak you done po'   Shine, __   Paid off ev-uh-

body ___   an' you did-n't   pay   Shine.

*Melody: Tonic chord (minor); the B♭ is an
attempt to notate the characteristic slide.*

We worked all summer an' all the Fall,
Got to take Christmas now in his overhalls.

"Captain, captain, is my money come?"
"Be here today, or tomorry one."

"Partner, partner, oh whar you goin'?"
"I'm goin' down the country whar they do pay mo'."

"Shine, you ought to be here when the captain paid off,
I got mo' money than the walkin' boss."

They ain't but one man that I do fear,
Big Jack Johnson, an' he ain't 'lowed here.

You can't do me lak you done po' Shine,
You taken his money, but you can't take mine.

Katie an' the Jim Lee Had a Little Race

Uncle John is eighty years old. He has a push cart in which he sometimes collects trash and garbage. This is the only kind of work he can
do now. He realizes that he is living in a changed world. He sang
"Katie an' the Jim Lee Had a Little Race" and then let his thoughts
turn back to the busy days of his youth. "Yes, Miss, I knowed this wuz
goin' to come to pass. I knowed it when they put them bridges all
across the rivuh. Trucks done took evuhthing—trucks an' busses. It
used to take a week to git freight frum Florence. We used to carry
lumber an' cotton seed. Now you kin git it in a day's time. Back in them

days the boats used to land right here. Ain't none uv it a-tall now."

In the busy days of the river, when a number of packets would be tied up at a wharf boat at the same time, all taking on or leaving freight, the Negroes with sacks on their shoulders would be running back and forth in what would seem utter confusion to an outsider. The roustabouts were usually required to keep in a trot. An old Negro woman who had been a chambermaid on the river for many years said, "Yes, honey, I kin remember them days. The rousters would be a-runnin' an' a-singin', a-runnin' an' a-singin'."

Most of the boats referred to in the lines of "Katie an' the Jim Lee Had a Little Race" can be identified with the Ohio and the Mississippi. The *Kate Adams* traveled on both rivers. The *James Lee* was built on the Ohio, at Jeffersonville, Indiana, for trade in the lower Mississippi. There were two packets named *Cherokee*. The first, a side-wheel steamer, was built at Cincinnati in 1873 and ran from that port to New Orleans. The second *Cherokee,* a stern-wheel boat, was built at Dubuque, Iowa, in 1888. Her home port was St. Louis, and she ran in the Mississippi River trade. The *Paul Tulane* was built at Jeffersonville in 1888. She was a sugar coast packet with New Orleans as her port of entry. The *Lady Lee* was also built at Jeffersonville, in 1889. Her home port was Memphis.

The boats of the Anchor Line,[5] beautiful side-wheelers, were named for various cities between St. Louis and New Orleans. The packets ran between these two points, touching the Ohio only at Cairo, Illinois, where the Ohio flows into the Mississippi.

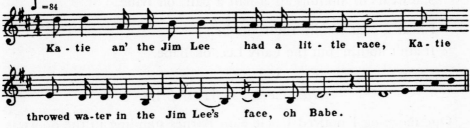

Ka-tie an' the Jim Lee had a lit-tle race, Ka-tie throwed wa-ter in the Jim Lee's face, oh Babe.

Melody: Pentatonic scale.

[5] A St. Louis shipbuilding corporation.

Way down the rivuh, jes' as fur as I kin see,
Don't see nothin' but the Cherokee, oh Babe.

Way down the rivuh, 'bout a hundred mile or mo',
Think I heard one Anchor Line blow, oh Babe.

Ef I wuz that Head Mate's son,
I'd stand on the head, an' see Katie when she run, oh Babe.

There's a big boat a-runnin', it's got no name,
But the boys all call it the Paul Tulane, oh Babe.

Told my woman when I lef' town,
I been a good ole wagon, but I mos' broke down, oh Babe.

Told my woman when I lef' town,
Make it to the levee when the Katie come down, oh Babe.

I bucked them dice, an' my point wuz fo',
Ella's in jail an' my money don't go, oh Babe.

That ole dame got mad at me,
I won ten dolluhs, wouldn't give her but three, oh Babe.

I'll be dogged ef I kin see,
How that money got away frum me, oh Babe.

A Dago woman an' a Dago man,
I spend my money at a Dago stand, oh Babe.

What kind uv shoes do my Ella wear?
She wears fo' dolluhs an' a half a pair, oh Babe.

I hear a boat comin' roun' the ben',
It ain't nothin' but the Lady Lee, oh Babe.

She Leaves Memphis

One morning I noticed Uncle Sam Barnes standing in the doorway
of his strange dwelling. The house had once been the rear part of a

grocery store. Now it is one small room, the door opening on the street, just a step above the sidewalk. There is a large padlock on the door. The lock seems to be merely a tribute to the conventions, for the door has no hinges. The room is papered with colored calendars of years past, and old newspapers. Sam was smoking a corncob pipe. "Yes'm, this have been a good pipe, but it's jes' lak I am now—done got ole."

Sam was on the river for many years in his youth.

"She Leaves Memphis," he says, was sung on the *Silver Cloud* and the *Clyde*.

The river packets carried twenty-five or thirty men to a watch. There were two watches, a forward and an after watch. The Negroes worked in shifts of six hours each, but when a stop was made at a large town where there would be a quantity of freight to move, the mate would call for "All Hands." About the work, Sam said, "They wuz two crews o' rousters, but when we would git into a freight pile, they wuzn't no rest fo' nobody." Often the work would continue through the night by the light of rosin torches placed along the bank.

She leaves Mem - phis an' she nev - uh make no stop. She got to Hel - en - a an' wuz due at Ea - gle Rock.——

Melody: Pentatonic scale—2d omitted.

Oh, Captain Agnew said when the Katie wuz made,
Arkansas City too short a trade.

Greenville will be some rouster's home,
Ain't comin' here no mo'.

Oh, big boat in the ben',
Ain't doin' nothin' but killin' men.

Vicksburg 'Round the Bend

Joe Hughes, a former rouster, is now living over a rather delapidated livery stable. His tasks are light and his wants are few. He feeds and waters the mules during the day, and on summer evenings he likes to bring his chair out on the sidewalk and sit near the curbstone.

After I had convinced Joe that I really wanted him to sing any songs of the river that he could remember, I found that he enjoys recalling them, and that sometimes he can sing one after another without hesitation. He sings in a rather quick tempo, and several repetitions are often necessary before a correct record can be obtained. When I attempted to verify my recording, by singing the songs for Joe's approval, it was not difficult to know whether he was pleased. If there were errors, he was serious, and made no comment, but unasked, sang the lines again, always at the same rapid pace. When he heard no mistakes, he looked incredulous; then his almost toothless smile grew broader. When he had no fault to find with the completed version, he laughed and shouted, "Lawd, jes' listen to her."

Oh, Vicks-burg is in the bend,— Natch-ez jes' be-low,— An-
go-la is a coun-ty farm, Oh Lawd, I don't want to go.—

Melody: Pentatonic scale—2d omitted.

Oh, tell my Baby, don't be oneasy, I'll be back some day.
Oh, when I leave here, I'm goin' back down the road.

Oh, Vicksburg is a hilly town,
An' the Yankees blowed it down, oh Lawd.

Oh, captain said when the Katie wuz made,
Arkansas City too short a trade.

Katie an' the Jim Lee had a race,
Katie throwed water in the Jim Lee's face.

Skinner, Skinner, You Know the Rule

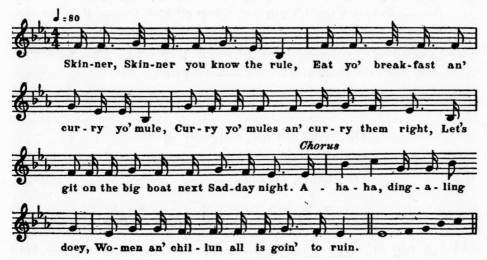

Skin-ner, Skin-ner you know the rule, Eat yo' break-fast an' cur-ry yo' mule, Cur-ry yo' mules an' cur-ry them right, Let's git on the big boat next Sad-day night. A - ha - ha, ding - a - ling doey, Wo-men an' chil-lun all is goin' to ruin.

Melody: Pentatonic scale—lacking characteristic skips.

What makes me lak my Baby so?
She does my washin', she pays my bo'd;
She pays my bo'd, she pays it right,
I'm goin' to git on the big boat next Sad-day night.

Singer omitted first two lines of this stanza.
Baby, Baby, bear this in mind,
Got a house full uv women, an' nary one mine.

Duke See the Tie Pile

Uncle Sims was known on the river long ago as Duke, because he was a familiar figure on the levee and wharf boat at Paducah, Kentucky. From his story we judge that this song came into being as an aid in loading ties. Sims says that he would always "feel mad" when he looked

at a large pile of ties, because, said he, "I knowed evuh one uv 'em had
to git on my shoulder."

Oh,__ Duke see the tie pile an' Duke git mad, Oh,___ Duke see the
mon-ey pile an' Duke git glad,   Oh ___Dad-dy, git   one.⁶

*Melody: Four tones of major scale.
Phrase groups of three.*

Oh, tain't no use in foolin' aroun',
Oh, all uv them ties got to go to town,
Oh Daddy, git one.

Master Had a Bran' New Coat

From Bill Sheffield, seventy-two years old, I learned "Master Had
a Bran' New Coat," which was sung on the *Kentucky,* the *Clyde,* and
the *City of Paducah.* I found the old fellow sitting on his porch washing
a pan of "greens." He would refill the tin pan with water from a
hydrant near the door, and as he drew the turnip leaves in and out of
the water, we talked about the days when he was "on the rivuh."

Bill said, "These here young niggers can't do the work we done. We
wuz better material than they is now. The Bible says the people gits
weaker an' wiser. At first they wuz giants; then they got down to double
jinted men. The Bible says to take no thought uv the remnants you
goin' to wear, but follow Me. Now-a-days evuhbody has to follow the
style, an' fust thing you know they got T.B. They didn't used to be
no sech thing. We wuzn't cold in the winter fo' we dressed warm. They
used to weave cloth on them big looms. I've carded many a spool fo' my
Mammy's spinnin' wheel. Young niggers today couldn't git up the

---

⁶ "Oh Daddy, git one," sung by one rouster when the tie had been lifted, was a signal to the
fellow next in line to pick up his own load.

hill with two hundred pounds on they back. Yes, Missy, we had to tote the freight up the hill, unless they wuz a wharf boat. The white folks wouldn't take no freight frum the water's edge."

Bill said that the rousters worked hard, but "they wuz always a boat ready to go, an' when we would git off one boat, pretty soon we'd take a notion an' ketch another."

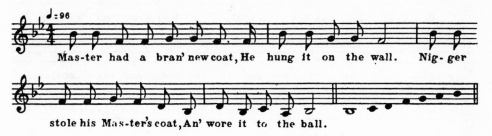

Mas-ter had a bran' new coat, He hung it on the wall. Nig-ger

stole his Mas-ter's coat, An' wore it to the ball.

Melody: Major scale—4th omitted.

> Where'd you git yo' whiskey,
> Where'd you git yo' dram?
> Where'd I git my whiskey?
> I got it frum Linkum Abraham.

God Dawg My Lousy Soul

This song, along with several others, was taken down from the singing of Uncle Tom Wall, nearly ninety years old. This particular song was sung on the *Silver Cloud* that burned at Birmingham, Kentucky, in 1887. Uncle Tom also roustered on the *W. A. Johnson* and the *City of Paducah*. The *W. A. Johnson* sailed from Paducah, and burned in the Tennessee River near Riverton. In speaking of the tragedy Tom said, "They wuz mules an' hosses on board, an' Oh Lawd, them geese a-squawkin'!"

Tom always spoke proudly of his job of the river days, as he was a lineman, and tied up the boat when she landed. During the last few years of his life, Uncle Tom worked at light jobs such as grass clipping in the cemetery that was near his small cottage. When questioned about some of the captains under whom he had worked in the old days, he pointed a trembling black finger over his shoulder toward the neatly trimmed grass plots with their white monuments, and said, "Why chile, they're all out there now."

God dawg my lous - y soul, God dawg my lous - y soul, An' she put me in the bed, An' she cov-ered up my head, God dawg my lous - y soul.

Melody: Major scale—7th omitted.

God dawg my lousy soul,
God dawg my lousy soul,
I'm goin' down the rivuh
An' I couldn't git across,
God dawg my lousy soul.

God dawg my lousy soul,
God dawg my lousy soul,
I jumped on that nigger,
I thought he wuz a horse,
God dawg my lousy soul.

God dawg my lousy soul,
God dawg my lousy soul,
I'm goin' down to Joppie,
An' I don't know fo' how long,
God dawg my lousy soul.

God dawg my lousy soul,[7]

[7] This stanza is irregular in verse form but is given here as it was sung.

God dawg my lousy soul,
I'm goin' to Missouri,
To git me another gal,
To sew on the sewin' machine.

To sew on the sewin' machine,[7]
To sew on the sewin' machine,
I'm goin' to Missouri,
To git me another dame,
To sew on the sewin' machine.

Ole Ada is a noble gal,[7]
Ole Ada is a noble gal,
An' she put me in the bed,
An' she covered up my head,
God dawg my lousy soul.

I'm the Man That Kin Raise So Long

"I'm the Man That Kin Raise So Long" and "I'm Goin' Down the Rivuh Befo' Long" are two labor songs sung by several former rousters as they sat on the porch of a cabin at the end of a lane far off the highway. Both sides of the narrow dirt road leading to the cottage were lined with white elder blossoms, and the delicate wild flower known as Queen Anne's Lace. Wild roses bloomed in thorny tangles, their faint color glowing through a yellow coating of Kentucky dust.

The darkies were expecting us, and some had gathered there to sing, a few others to listen. One barefooted colored woman evidently had tasks to do, but was unwilling to stay away, so she sat under a tree near the porch, and there with a bucket of water and a pan as equipment, she unconcernedly picked a chicken—now and then joining in the conversation without stopping her work.

"I'm the Man That Kin Raise So Long" was sung on the *Stacker Lee* and the *Ferd Herold*.

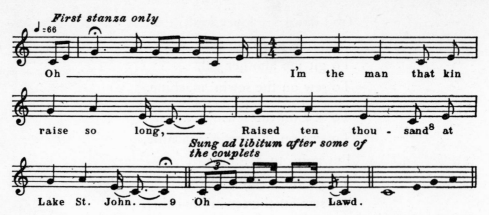

Melody: Tonic chord with added 6th.

Oh, boat's up the rivuh an' she won't come down,
She got a head lead uv water an' she droppin' on down.

Oh, tell my Baby, don't be oneasy,
I'll be home some day.

White folks got all the cotton an' corn,
Oh, nigger run away wid the taters.

Oh, come here dog an' git yo' bone,
Tell me what shoulder you want it on.[10]

Oh Lawd, this time tomorry evenin',
I'll be on my way back home.

Oh Lawd, I didn't know
I had to bow so low.[11]

[8] Pounds of cotton.

[9] Just above Natchez.

[10] This line occurs in many rouster songs. It suggests the carrying of a sack or some other heavy weight on alternate shoulders during the handling of a cargo.

[11] Bend under a load.

SUNSET ON THE RIVUH

I'm Goin' Down the Rivuh Befo' Long

Melody: Pentatonic scale. Phrase groups of three.

I'm goin' where the chilly winds don't blow, oh Baby,
Goin' where the chilly winds don't blow,
I'm goin' where the chilly winds don't blow.

Ain't comin' back till 'bout in the fall, oh Baby,
Ain't comin' back till 'bout in the fall,
Ain't comin' back till 'bout in the fall.

I'm goin' down the rivuh to carry some sacks, oh Baby,
Goin' down the rivuh to carry some sacks,
I'm goin' down the rivuh to carry some sacks.

I'll have the money when I git back, oh Baby,
I'll have the money when I git back,
I'll have the money when I git back.

Carryin' Sacks

"Carryin' Sacks" was sung by a former rouster on the *W. F. Nisbet*. The *Nisbet* was built in 1889, at Evansville, Indiana. Her trade included the section between Shawneetown Bend and Johnsonville, Tennessee. This was the river's greatest corn country. On one trip the *Nisbet* took on four thousand sacks of corn within the distance of a half mile.

Corn, shelled and on the ear, potatoes, and other products were shipped for convenience in sacks that could be lifted and "toted" on strong black shoulders. The sacks usually weighed about 150 pounds. In addition to the usual wage of a dollar and a half a day, the Negroes were sometimes paid a penny extra for every sack they carried in loading and unloading the cargo. They speak of this arrangement as "a penny off an' a penny on."

I'm goin' up the riv-uh to car-ry them sacks,
I'm goin' up the riv-uh to car-ry them sacks, I'm
goin' up the riv-uh to car-ry them sacks, I'll have yo'
lap full uv dol-luhs when I git back.

Melody: Natural minor scale—2d and 6th omitted.

I went up the rivuh an' made a broken trip,
I went up the rivuh an' made a broken trip,
I went up the rivuh an' made a broken trip,
I lost my sugar fo' my foot had slipped.

I asked my sugar fo' a little kiss,
I asked my sugar fo' a little kiss,
I asked my sugar fo' a little kiss,
She said, "Baby, you go an' come agin.

You go back up the rivuh an' carry some sacks,
You go back up the rivuh an' carry some sacks,
You go back up the rivuh an' carry some sacks,
You kin git my kisses when the boat gits back."

I'm Goin' Up the Rivuh

I learned this song from Uncle Barney Allison. He is known among the Negroes as "Doc," because, they will tell you, he is an herb doctor. Barney said, "Yaas'm, I doctors. Fo' a long time now, evuh since I quit the rivuh, I ain't done nothin' else but doctor. I goes out in the woods an' stays near 'bout all day. I digs down an' gits the herbs,—'bout fifteen diffunt kinds uv 'em. I cooks 'em down fo' medecin. I knows jes' how to fix 'em. The fust man I cured wuz when I wuz 'leven year ole. I had to go all the way out to Rattle Snake Hill to git the herbs fo' him, an' when he wuz well he give me a new suit uv clothes. The herbs don't grow 'ceptin' where they is snakes.

"You kin read in the Book 'bout the herbs. They is all numbered an' when you comes to a pizen number you mustn't tech it. The Book says they is a herb fo' evuh disease on the earth. They is a herb fo' consumption, but I ain't nevuh come acrosst it yit. They is one fo' a bad cold, but the Book says won't nobody nevuh find that root till the end uv time. The drug sto' man keeps a-tryin' to cure a bad cold. I won't say he don't try, but he ain't nevuh foun' nothin'.

"No'm, nobody nevuh taught me how to doctor people. It wuz with me when I wuz born. I'm the seventh son, an' I wuz born with a double veil on my face. Evuh seventh son born with a veil has sech a strong Power uv the Sperit that they has to have a godmother to keep 'em frum dyin'. The Sperit is so strong in 'em it kills 'em, ef they ain't a godmother to take keer uv 'em. My godmother had to raise me till I wuz seventeen year ole. Sometimes when I puts out my han' fo' a herb, a voice says to me, 'Don't tech that one.' I kin hear it, an' it comes to me jes' what to do.

"Evuhthing that is happenin' in the whole worl' is in the Book. It says evuh nation goin' to be at war, an' when the las' battle is fitten the sun will be red as blood, an' at twelve o'clock in the day it will be dark as midnight. Yaas, Lawd, evuhthing the Book says is slippin' up on us. They won't evuhbody be killed. Even when the las' battle is fitten they will be some left, but the Book says we has to ride through blood up to the saddle skirts. They ain't no herb to keep people frum fightin'."

"I'm goin' up the rivuh" or "down the rivuh" are favorite beginnings for songs in various moods—usually plaints containing familiar lines that mirror the hardships of the life of the deck hand.

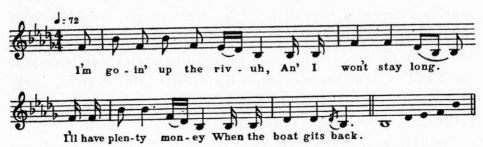

I'm goin' up the riv-uh, An' I won't stay long.
I'll have plen-ty mon-ey When the boat gits back.

Melody: Tonic chord (minor)—4th degree used as a passing tone.

I've packed so many sacks
Until it made my shoulder so',
But this heavy load
I can't carry no mo'.

Ef I don't make but fifteen cents,
Baby, you kin have a dime.
Run here an' git yo' bone,
Tell what shoulder you want it on.

I Wuz Borned on the Rivuh

Aunt Nancy usually spent the summer afternoons sitting, barefooted, on her porch. I often stopped by to see her, and to hear her stories of the days when she "wuz on the rivuh."

I noticed that she always wore a nutmeg around her neck. A hole had been cut through it, and it hung from a soiled white string. When I asked her why she wore it, she said, "Why honey, that's to keep me frum ketchin' cole. I know the white folks don't b'lieve all the things the Naps[12] b'lieve in, but this worl' is full uv meanness. They's too many hoodoo-ers right heah in this town. It all goes back to the Bible. The fust time they got in behind me, I come down drinlin' sick.[13] I used to be a good lookin' nigger, an' a straight-up nigger. When they put the mojo[14] on me, I wuz all bent ovuh. I went out to see the herb doctuh that lives down by Mosquito Bottom, an' he said, 'You jes' did git heah in time.' Then he said, 'Now I'm goin' to show you who done it.' He had a big green rock, 'bout as big as my two han's. I looked in the rock, an' I seen her. He said to me, 'I see a quilt with blue in it.' That wuz true, so he'p me God. He said, 'Boil that quilt in red pepper an' salt, then open up yo' feather bolster, an' bring me what you finds in it.' When I cut that bolster open, thar it wuz. It looked like red flannel on one side, an' lace on the othuh. As soon as he seen it, he said, 'They sho' throwed at you, an' throwed at you hard.' Then he tole me to drap it in runnin' watuh, an' aftuh I drapped it in, not to nevuh look back.

"Aftuh I done throwed it in the rivuh, I had a vision. The Mastuh tole me that they would try to hurt me with the mojo seven times, an'

[12] The darkie's own word for those of his race. It refers to "nappy haired" or the thick woolly hair of the Negro.

[13] An illness resulting from the work of a mojo in the possession of an enemy, or a spell cast by a conjurer. The illness is a slow wasting away. A healthy person becomes stooped over, slow moving, weak, and "jes' drinels away to nothin'." If discovered in time, a drink of melted hog lard will break the spell "when nothin' else will."

[14] A charm obtained from a conjurer, that has power to bring anything desired to the person who carries it. The mojo can also be used to bring ill fortune to an enemy, if it is prepared by the conjurer for that purpose. Men usually carry a mojo in a pocket where there is no chance of it being discovered. Women, as a rule, tie them to their body, on the left side, just in front of the hip bone. No one but the owner is ever allowed to see it.

Mojos are made in various ways, depending upon the formula of the conjurer who creates it, and the purpose for which it is intended. It often consists of a piece of dried skin of a lizard or snake; sometimes it is made of needles. The charm is enclosed in a small bag, usually of red flannel. A loadstone is a potent mojo, and herbs of many kinds are used. If the disruption of a home is desired, the mojo is made from a rare, slender root called "Devil's Shoe String."

One of the most powerful mojos is made from the good luck bone of a black cat. Every black cat has one lucky, or magic, bone. To find it, the cat must be boiled alive, "until all the meat falls off." Then the bones are taken to a "branch," or small stream. One bone at a time is held under the water. When the lucky bone touches the water, the stream immediately begins to flow uphill. The lucky bone, thus identified, is then sewed up in a flannel bag.

He showed me the one that wuz tryin' it. I said, 'Thank you, Mastuh, fo' showin' me.' Yes Lawd, whatevah goes ovuh the Devil's back, comes 'round unduh his belly, an' buckled tight. People that wears a mojo is always studyin' meanness. Most uv the time they is made uv turtle meat, an' them that's got it in 'em, has a face fo' evuhbody.

"Thar's a woman right up this street that's got a mojo on her. One day the conjur[15] woman went out an' measured her footprint in the dust. She said, 'I've got jes' enough fo' her.' Well fo' God an' man, that gal ain't nevuh walked since, an' nevuh will walk again."

Aunt Nancy used to be a maid on the Ohio River boats. When she sang for me she was always interested in watching me write down the words and music. The first time she realized that I was setting down just what she sang, she said, "Fo' God, I'm composin' music."

Asked just where she had learned this song, she answered, "Oh chile, them rousters wuz always a-singin' it."

I wuz borned on the riv-uh, An' the riv-uh is my home, As long as I kin car-ry a chain I won't let the riv-uh a-lone.

Melody: Tonic chord (major) with added 6th.

Oh captain, captain,
Have the money come?
The reason why I asked you,
I want to borry some.

[15] "Conjur" woman (from our word "conjure") means one who has power to command a devil, or spirit, or to cast a spell. Conjurers are usually a seventh son, or a seventh daughter. This gives them supernatural power. They are also known as "two-headed people."

Well, the captain is a-standin'
Up on the harrykin roof,[16]
He's a-hollerin' down on the deckhead
Tellin' the boys what to do.

Oh let us hurry, boys,
Ef you want to git home,
Le's load the boat out,
Let the dice an' cards alone.

Oh, Annie, Oh!

Aunt Belle Terry has never worked on any of the boats, and has never traveled far from her home, but she has always lived near the river bank, and for many years she used to bring butter, milk, and eggs down to the landing for the boats to pick up when they stopped for passengers or freight. Aunt Belle was seven years old when the war began in 1861, and she can remember most of the famous Ohio River packets. "The white folks tells me that I've got the bes' recollection they evuh seen."

I took down "Oh, Annie, Oh!" and "Down the Rivuh, Down, Boys" on Belle's porch one summer morning. Whenever she would come to a line she wanted to emphasize, she would reach out and touch my arm with her stiff brown fingers. Before she had finished singing, a little group had gathered to listen—two Negro women from next door, and several barefooted kinky-haired children. The children were all eating green apples that had fallen from the tree near the steps, and they stared at me silently.

Just a few days before, I had stopped by to see Aunt Belle after supper. I had been unable to finish writing down the song she was singing at that time, because it had gradually grown too dark. As I was leaving, Belle dispatched her grandson to a neighbor's to borrow

[16] Hurricane deck.

some coal oil so that she could light her lamp. Next morning I noticed
a lamp burning dimly on a table inside the door. Remembering my
previous visit, I asked Aunt Belle if she wanted me to blow out the
flame. She said, "Jes' set still, honey; I'm lettin' it burn so's I kin start
a fiah to cook some meat fo' dinnuh; I ain't got no matches."

When she had finished singing, Aunt Belle leaned back in her rocking
chair and said, "Lawd chile, my mammy nevuh carried me off on the
big watuhs but one time, an' then she nevuh tole me whar it wuz at.
I wuz borned on the fust day uv the week, an' the fust day uv the month,
an' the fust day uv the year. Ef folks got any kine uv misery uh any kine
uv hurtin' I kin put my han' on 'em an' it'll go away. I wuz borned that
way. A woman come to me the othuh day with a cancer on huh arm.
I tuk hole uv huh han' and squez it, an' huh arm stopped burnin'.
She's comin' back today an' I'm goin' to rub it an' tell huh to put some
green tomato on it. The cancer'll go away. No, honey, I don't know
nothin' 'bout how I does it. Nobody can't tell nothin' 'bout what they
wuz borned with."

The melodies of these two songs are something alike. When Aunt
Belle sings, her voice seems to wander around in a rather aimless
fashion with an unconscious preference for the tones of the tonic chord.
But she sings in a very definite rhythm and in a spirited tempo.

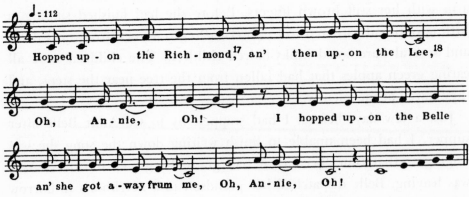

Melody: Major scale—2d and 7th omitted.

Belle's so fast she got no time,
Oh, Annie, Oh!
Han' me down a dolluh an' a dime,
Oh, Annie, Oh!

Han' me down a dolluh an' a dime,
Oh, Annie, Oh!
Give me the sign, an' the money's mine,[19]
Oh, Annie, Oh!

Han' me down a dolluh an' a dime,
Oh, Annie, Oh!
It's a dolluh a day, work or play,[20]
Oh, Annie, Oh!

I'm goin' to ship on the Eagle Tender,[21]
Oh, Annie, Oh!
Buy my wife a Grecian Bender,[22]
Oh, Annie, Oh!

---

[17] A very fine side-wheel packet with the words "Low Pressure" painted on her wheelhouses. The *Richmond* was built at Madison, Indiana, in 1867.

[18] Although many boats carried the name of Lee, probably this refers to the *Belle Lee,* a beautiful side-wheeler built at New Albany, Indiana, in 1863.

[19] The mates remembered the faces of many of the rousters from previous trips, and when the Negroes were applying again for work, often a nod or a sign from the mate would be all the contract that was necessary.

[20] Rousters were paid by the day, regardless of the length of the trip, or amount of freight handled. As the song says, it was "a dolluh a day, work or play."

[21] No doubt refers to the steamer *Legal Tender* built at New Albany, Indiana, in 1869.

[22] The Grecian Bend was in fashion about 1868. It was a stilted artificial manner of carrying the body, bent forward from the hips.

Down the Rivuh, Down, Boys

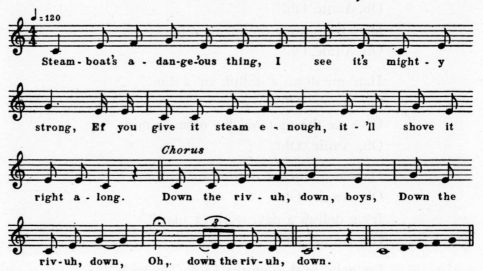

Steam-boat's a - dan-ge-'ous thing, I see it's might-y strong, Ef you give it steam e - nough, it - 'll shove it right a - long.

Chorus

Down the riv - uh, down, boys, Down the riv-uh, down, Oh, down the riv-uh, down.

Melody: Major scale—6th and 7th omitted.

Conscripts[23] a-comin' an' I hear it evuh day,

Them that take a notice will try an' git away.

[23] Soldiers during the years 1861-65.

3

Songs of Boats

IT IS difficult for us to realize now how important the steamboats were to the river valley. They were associated with romance, trade, and adventure. Much of the business life of the towns centered around the arrival and departure of the packets.

Boats have always possessed a strange power of calling forth the loyalty of their crews. To the Negroes the handling of a large cargo meant hard work, excitement, and, what was considered then, high wages; they knew the routes of the packets and which ones held records for speed.

It was very usual for the Negro babies in the valley to be named for some of the important boats. Many packets carried the names of their owners, but the little children were named for the boat itself, not the man who owned her.

The names of boats occur often in the music of the river, but in some of the songs the Negroes give us, unconsciously, a picture of the dangers and hardships of a voyage. It is natural that there are wailing lines of boats aground. This was a disaster that frequently delayed packets for days at a time when the water was low.

Whenever a boat sank, the story was recorded in song; and from the rousters' singing we learn much of that most dreaded of tragedies, a boat in flames. As a rule, the cargo of a packet offered little resistance to fire. But the extreme danger was in the desire for speed. Overheated

engines and exploding boilers on boats that were in themselves highly
inflammable were the cause of heartbreaking losses in life and property.
The small volume published in 1856, James T. Lloyd's *Steamboat
Directory and Disasters on Western Waters,* gives us a sad insight into
the tragedy of fire on the river.

B'y'[1] Sara Burned Down

The *City of Bayou Sara* was a beautiful side-wheel packet, owned by
the St. Louis and New Orleans Anchor Line. She was built in Jeffersonville, Indiana, in 1884, and on December 5, 1885, she caught fire while
carrying a cargo of hay and other inflammable freight, and burned to
the water's edge. The disaster occurred at 11 o'clock at night, near
the shore, at New Madrid, Missouri. Under the command of Captain
J. Baker all the passengers and the greater part of the crew were saved.
Some of the rousters who were sleeping on one of the decks were late
in receiving the alarm and were unsuccessful in getting to shore.

Colin Robinson, an old Negro now living in a small town on the
Ohio, was a rouster on this ill-fated voyage. He says, "It wuz a long
time ago, an' I was jes' a boy. Some o' them rousters wuz sleepin' so
heavy we nevuh got 'em out in time." Colin explained that the rousters
always had to sleep anywhere they could, and "slep' heavy," sometimes
because of more than enough whiskey, and often because "they wuz
broke down frum the work."

Colin says that the steamer *Arkansas City* came to the aid of the
unfortunate boat. Some of the rescued passengers were brought to
Memphis; others went on to Vicksburg where they took another packet
to New Orleans.

Safe aboard the *Arkansas City,* with the vivid memory of the disaster
fresh in their minds, it was natural that the rousters would find an
emotional release in creating a song about the tragedy. While the
rousters were soothed and calmed by the singing, the mate of the

[1] The Negro's pronunciation of the word "Bayou" (Bī' ōō).

FORMER ROUSTER'S GRANDSON

"B'y' Sara," Mr. Tobe Royal, was distressed at hearing the sad story constantly retold in song. Colin says, "We had to make up this song when the mate wuzn't aroun' fo' he said he didn' want to hear no song 'bout the 'B'y' Sara,' an' he wuz goin' to whup any rouster he caught singin' about the fire."

In spite of this warning, the song was not silenced and gradually became better known as the rousters of the *City of Bayou Sara* traveled.

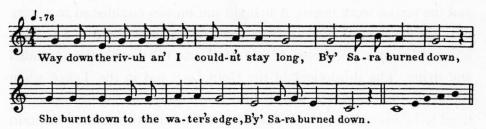

Way down the riv-uh an' I could-n't stay long, B'y' Sa-ra burned down,
She burnt down to the wa-ter's edge, B'y' Sa-ra burned down.

Melody: Tonic chord (major)—6th and 7th added.

The people begun to run an' squall,
B'y' Sara burned down,
When they begin to look they wuz about to fall,
B'y' Sara burned down.

Look away over yonder, what I see,
B'y' Sara burned down,
The captain an' the mate wuz comin' after me,
B'y' Sara burned down.

There's two bright angels by my side,
B'y' Sara burned down,
'Cause I want to go to Heaven when I die,
B'y' Sara burned down.

The Gold Dust Fire

The packet *Gold Dust* was destroyed by explosion of her boilers just after leaving Hickman, Kentucky. Seventeen were killed, and forty-seven wounded. The disaster occurred August 7, 1882.

That summer afternoon a child was playing under the shade trees of lovely Maple Hall, that overlooked the Mississippi. She climbed up on the tall gate post to wave at the white packet as she passed. Just at that moment the boat lurched and rocked strangely. The child cried out in fright, and her father, Dr. Alexander Allen Faris, ran from the house down toward the river bank.

He organized a fleet of skiffs, manned each of them with two men, and the rescue work began. A first-aid station was established in a store near the levee, and the survivors were taken from there to Dr. Faris home. Within a few hours Maple Hall was filled with the wounded and dying. The third clerk of the *Gold Dust* was in the Texas[2] when the explosion came. He was thrown down into the engine room. He lived to be brought to Maple Hall, but died a short time later. Captain McCord, in command of the boat, was painfully injured by burns on his hands and feet, but he recovered.

The first clerk, John A. Langlois, was seriously burned from scalding water. Langlois, a Frenchman, was a Mississippi River man of intense Southern sympathy. In 1863 he had put the boat he was commanding at the disposal of a young man who was attempting to make his way past enemy lines with a message of vital importance to the Confederacy. This daring young soldier was Alexander Allen Faris, later an Anchor Line surgeon and the owner of Maple Hall.

Faris had been a soldier in the Confederate army. He lost his right arm from wounds in 1862, but continued to serve the Southern Cause until the end of the war as a dispatch bearer in Kentucky and West Tennessee for Cheatham's Army. Soon after the close of the war Faris resumed his study of medicine, begun four years before. He became a skillful surgeon and it is said that he performed, with his left hand, every brain operation then known to the medical profession.

---

[2] On the first steamboats the rooms for the passengers were identified by giving each room the name of one of the states of the Union—hence the term "stateroom." Rooms for the officers of the boat were provided on the upper deck, or hurricane roof. Because these quarters had to be adequate for all of the officers, the name of the largest state was reserved for this section of the boat. It is therefore called the "Texas."

Dr. Faris used his home, Maple Hall, as a hospital for the survivors of the *Gold Dust* disaster as long as the need existed. Langlois was a welcomed guest there until he was able to walk again, fourteen months later.

When Samuel Clemens (Mark Twain) desired to visit again some of the river towns he had known years before as a Mississippi River pilot, he made a part of his journey on the *Gold Dust,* just three months before her tragic fire. The interesting account of this journey, as well as an account of the disaster, have become familiar to us through Mark Twain's *Life on the Mississippi.*

The loss of the *Gold Dust* made a vivid impression on the minds of the Negroes. Rousters memorialized the tragedy in this song which was afterwards sung on various boats.

Ain't that a pit-y, oh Lawd, Ain't that a pit-y,

oh Lawd, Ain't that a pit-y, oh Lawd, Ain't that a

pit-y 'bout the Gold Dust men. Some got scald-ed, Some got

drown-ded, Some got burnt up in the Gold Dust fire.

Melody: First six tones from major scale—tonic chord entirely, except for sequence in measure three.

John Gilbert

The *John Gilbert* ran from Cincinnati to Florence, Alabama. She was built in Pittsburgh, Pennsylvania, in 1881, and was named for

Captain John Gilbert, of Evansville, Indiana, president of the Ohio and Tennessee River Packet Company.

A certain section through which this boat passed was known for its trade in peanuts. The *John Gilbert* was loaded with this product by the thousand pounds and the vessel was nicknamed by the rousters, "The Peanut John." It is said that on one trip the *John Gilbert* carried the largest cargo of peanuts ever received in Cincinnati. All available space on the main deck,[3] boiler deck, and hurricane deck was used to store the cargo. Two thousand sacks of peanuts were taken on at Britt's Landing, over five thousand more up the Tennessee at Sycamore, and another load at Johnsonville.

After the *Clyde* sank, the *John Gilbert* was chartered for the Paducah to St. Louis trade. In less than a year she went down in the Mississippi River opposite Goose Island, near a narrow strip of water known as "Chester Chute." This was considered a dangerous place in the river, and many boats have been lost there. The darkies say that at this point there "wuz a drawin' to bottom an' a halfway suck."

On this last trip the *John Gilbert* struck a reef and grounded. The strong current swung her around and she broke in two.

Among the rousters there are many stories of boats that "broke in two," but steamboat captains say that records of this particular disaster are very rare. The cause of a packet "breaking in two" is supposed to be faulty loading of an extremely heavy cargo.

After the *John Gilbert* went aground, her passengers were taken to St. Louis by the packet *New South*. Two members of the crew stayed on the sand bar to watch the wreck. When the *New South* stopped and offered assistance, the pilot of the *John Gilbert,* Mr. Sam Briscoe, said to the captain of the rescue boat, "What do you think of my monument?"

Uncle Tom Wall, from whose singing this song was taken down,

---

[3] The decks of a steamboat from the waterline up are designated as follows: Lower, or main deck; second, or boiler deck is just above the boilers, where the passenger cabins are located; top deck, or hurricane roof, is the Texas, or officers' quarters; the pilot house is right in front of the Texas, or above it.

had made many trips on the *John Gilbert,* but he left her before the disaster. When questioned about this, he said, "She wuz a purty boat an' a fas' boat, but I wouldn't make no mo' trips on her after I seen them bad luck tricks." According to Uncle Tom, some props had fallen off at Jeffersonville, and a short time later three rats had jumped from the "nose uv the boat." Pressed for his explanation of the ancient mystery of rats leaving the sinking ship, Uncle Tom said, "I don't know, chile, a warnin' frum the Lawd God, I reckon."

"John Gilbert" is primarily a song of a well-known packet, but it is also a labor song.

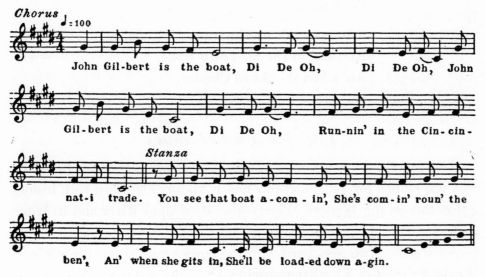

Melody: Natural minor scale—2d and 6th omitted. Chorus in parallel phrases of three divisions—second phrase extended to four measures. Rondo form.

> Lee P. Kahn wuz the head clerk,
> Captain Duncan wuz the captain,
> Billy Evit wuz the head mate,
> Runnin' in the Cincinnati trade.
>
> She hauled peanuts an' cotton,
> An' she hauled so many

When she got to Johnsonville,
Her work would just begin.

She hauled so many peanuts
Her men run frum her,
They went out in the wilderness,
An' they nevuh come back no mo'.

She hauled so many peanuts,
The rousters run frum her,
They couldn't git nobody to load her,
But the free labors.[4]

They put her to Florence, Alabama,
Runnin' in the St. Louis trade,
An' when she got to Chester,
She broke half in two.

The Joe Fowler Blues

The *Joe Fowler* was one of the most popular packets on the river. She was named for a member of a family vividly identified with historical events on the Western Waters—the Mississippi River and its tributaries.

Among the boats associated with the Fowler family[5] was the gunboat, *Little Rebel*, C.S.N.,[6] that participated in the naval battle of Island

[4] Men not regularly employed on the boat, or men taken on from the shore for an emergency.
[5] Boats owned and commanded by the Fowler family:
1859—*Silver Star*, Evansville-Paducah trade, commanded by Captain Gus Fowler.
1860—*Dunbar*, Evansville-Paducah trade, commanded by Captain Gus Fowler; *Alvin Adams*, St. Louis-Nashville, St. Louis-New Orleans trade, commanded by Captain J. Whyte Fowler, C.S.N.; gunboat *Little Rebel*, flagship of the Confederate fleet, commanded by Captain J. Whyte Fowler.
1861—*Arkansas Ram*, C.S.N., partly built by Captain Dick Fowler.
1870—*Idlewilde*, Paducah-Cairo trade, built and commanded by Captain Gus Fowler.
1876—*Pat Cleburne*, commanded by Captain Dick Fowler, who was burned to death when this boat exploded her boilers, May, 1876; *Armada*, commanded by Captain W. P. Fowler.
Other boats partly owned and controlled by the Fowlers: *James Fisk, Jr., John Gilbert, Gus Fowler, Silver Cloud, Joe Fowler, Red Cloud, Dick Fowler, Robert Mitchell, John S. Hopkins, Rapidan No. 1.*
[6] Confederate States Navy.

No. 10, 1862. After this battle the *Little Rebel* went to the defense of Memphis, and was captured when that city surrendered. The gun-boat at this time was under command of Captain James Whyte Fowler, a brother of the man for whom the steamboat *Joe Fowler* was named. When the *Little Rebel* fell into the hands of the Union forces, Captain Fowler made his escape by jumping overboard. Two years later he was killed in action. Captain Fowler was once described as "the most attractive man that ever trod the hurricane deck of a steamboat."

Dickson Given Fowler and Littleton Augustus Fowler, brothers of Captain Fowler, were also officers in the Confederate service. It was for these two men that the packets, *Dick Fowler* and *Gus Fowler* were named.

In the spring of 1865, just after General Johnston had surrendered his army in North Carolina, Major Littleton Augustus Fowler, known on the rivers as "Captain Gus," was making his way to Baltimore along with some other officers of the C.S.A. On April 14, the world was shocked and grieved at the assassination of President Lincoln by John Wilkes Booth at the Ford Theater in Washington. Since a large reward was offered for his capture, every effort was made by police and detective agencies to locate and bring Booth back alive. Because of a striking resemblance to Booth, Major Fowler was followed by detectives for several days. He was carefully watched, and a number of times his life was in danger, until the detectives were finally convinced of their mistake.

Captain Gus Fowler was commanding the side-wheel packet *Dunbar* in 1861. The *Dunbar,* owned by the Fowler family, was in the lower Ohio when word reached her that war had been declared. So that the boat would not be captured by Union forces, Captain Fowler ran her up the river and sunk her by cutting a hole in her hull. He then enlisted in the Confederate service. Later he learned that the *Dunbar* had been raised and was being used by the United States Navy as a gunboat.

The first year of the war, Paducah, the home town of the Fowlers, was occupied by Union forces. The story of the day General Grant landed at the wharf boat can still be heard in the town. One account tells us: "The soldiers came from the boats four abreast, with the bayonets on their rifles flashing in the sunlight. They came out as thick as bees from the hive." General Grant stopped at the top of the levee, and read a proclamation that was intended to reassure the people of the community. As he was promising them protection, he was interrupted by a citizen who shouted, "To Hell with such protection!"

The *Joe Fowler*, built at Jeffersonville, Indiana, in 1888, was a vessel of 356 tons, 182 feet long, and 31.6 feet wide. She was known as the fastest stern-wheeler on Western Waters, and until about the year 1904, carried the U.S. mail between Evansville, Indiana, and Paducah, Kentucky. On her maiden trip down the Ohio, she received ovations from crowds along the banks; and when she reached Paducah, under full steam with flags flying, she was greeted by whistles from steamboats and factories, and the shouts of hundreds of people waiting on the levee to welcome her. One account of this journey tells us that the *Joe Fowler* "flew down the river like a fawn."

The boat was built for a passenger steamer but she also carried freight. Her largest cargoes were cattle and hogsheads of tobacco. In harvest seasons she carried a great deal of corn and wheat. This packet was known among the rousters as "Jumpin' Joe." This nickname followed her because she moved with such speed that great waves were left in her path. It is said that for this reason she was not popular with the "shanty boat dwellers," who were inconvenienced by so much commotion in the water.

The whistle of the *Joe Fowler* gave just one very long blast. This was the call of all the Fowler boats, but it is said that the "Jumpin' Joe" always sounded a note that was especially distinctive and musical.

The *Joe Fowler* was a luxurious boat, and every care was taken to insure the comfort and pleasure of her passengers. The ladies' cabins were beautifully equipped, and in the main salon the white and gold woodwork was carved in delicate and exquisite designs. Every evening after dinner music for dancing was provided by some of the colored

PADUCAH RIVER FRONT, 1873

"cabin boys," and there was always one among them who, for a few thrilling moments, was allowed to occupy the center of the floor and "do the cakewalk." In the nineties the cakewalk was at the height of its popularity, and was strictly a Negro dance.

The *Joe Fowler* made regular round trips with passengers and freight, from Louisville to Pittsburgh, and she was always in demand at Mardi Gras seasons for the trip to New Orleans. During the first World War she was assigned to the duty of moving barges loaded with steel down the Ohio from Pittsburgh. Because of the great power of her engine, she was especially valuable for this service.

When the operation of packet boats became unprofitable because of the decline in passenger and freight business, the *Joe Fowler* was converted into an excursion boat. Her name was changed to *Crescent* and she traveled out of Evansville for some years. In 1920 she was destroyed by fire. No part of the splendid boat was saved, not even the famous whistle that had sounded gallantly along the rivers for twenty-eight years.

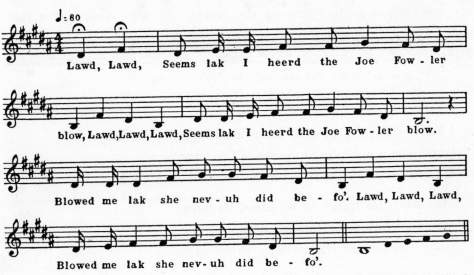

Lawd, Lawd, Seems lak I heerd the Joe Fow-ler blow, Lawd, Lawd, Lawd, Seems lak I heerd the Joe Fow-ler blow. Blowed me lak she nev-uh did be-fo'. Lawd, Lawd, Lawd, Blowed me lak she nev-uh did be-fo'.

Melody: Major scale—2d and 7th omitted.

Lawd, Lawd,

Blowed lak she had my Baby on bo'd, Lawd, Lawd, Lawd,

Blowed lak she had my Baby on bo'd.

I know you goin' to miss me when I'm gone, Lawd, Lawd, Lawd,

Know you goin' to miss me when I'm gone.

Lawd, Lawd,

Miss me frum rollin' in yo' arms, Lawd, Lawd, Lawd,

Miss me frum rollin' in yo' arms.

Fare thee well, honey, fare thee well, Lawd, Lawd, Lawd,

Fare thee well, my honey, fare thee well.

I'm Goin' Down the Rivuh

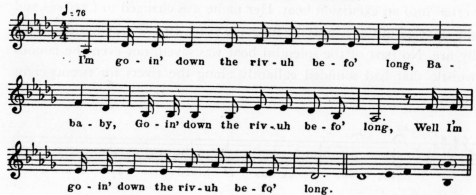

Melody: Pentatonic scale.
Phrase groups of three.

I know you goin' to miss me when I'm gone, Ba-Baby,

Know you goin' to miss me when I'm gone,

Well, I know you goin' to miss me when I'm gone.

Miss me frum rollin' in yo' arms, Ba-Baby,

Miss me frum rollin' in yo' arms,

Goin' to miss me frum rollin' in yo' arms.

I think I heerd the Joe Fowler blow, Lawd, Lawd, Lawd,

I think I heerd the Joe Fowler blow,

I think I heerd the Joe Fowler blow.

She blowed lak she ain't goin' to blow no mo', Lawd, Lawd, Lawd,
She blowed lak she ain't goin' to blow no mo',
She blowed lak she ain't goin' to blow no mo'.

Oh, times ain't lak they used to be, Ba-Baby,
Oh, times ain't lak they used to be,
Oh, times ain't lak they used to be.

Oh, I used to make a dolluh evuh day, Ba-by,
Oh, I used to make a dolluh evuh day,
Oh, I used to make a dolluh evuh day.

Treat me right, I'd ruther work than play, Lawd, Lawd, Lawd,
Treat me right, I'd ruther work than play,
Treat me right, I'd ruther work than play.

You mistreated me without a cause, Lawd, Lawd, Lawd,
You mistreated me without a cause,
You mistreated me without a cause.

'Cause you goin' to miss me when I'm gone, Lawd, Lawd, Lawd,
'Cause you goin' to miss me when I'm gone,
'Cause you goin' to miss me when I'm gone.

Golden City

A striking similarity exists between the melody of "Golden City" and the song "Oh Dem Golden Slippers" by the Negro song writer James A. Bland. Information as to which song was sung first is not available. The *Golden City* was built in Cincinnati in 1876 and burned at Memphis in 1882. "Oh Dem Golden Slippers" was published in 1879.

The steamboats, *Golden City, Golden Crown,* and *Paris C. Brown,* were built to travel in the Cincinnati-Memphis trade. Memphis was the port of entrance, and Cincinnati was considered the home port as the rousters were always paid off there. The *Golden City,* a stern-wheel packet, and the *Golden Crown* brought sugar and cotton from Memphis to Cincinnati, stopping at Louisville and other points on the way. On the return trip the cargo was varied, with a large quantity, as a rule, of buggies and wagons.

Many boats were known by nicknames given them by the rousters. For example, the *W. A. Johnson* was known during her lifetime as the "Pig Iron Johnson." The reason for this title was the large quantity of pig iron the vessel carried to Paducah and Evansville from the furnace in La Grange. The *W. A. Johnson* was built at Jeffersonville, Indiana, for the trade between Paducah, Kentucky, and Florence, Alabama. Paducah was her home port, and on the journey to Florence the cargo was usually groceries.

The *Golden City,* the *W. A. Johnson,* and the *Paris C. Brown* were all destroyed by fire. It happened that the "Pig Iron Johnson" had been taken to a point in midstream during the evening before the boat caught fire. Because of this, the rousters believed the fire was not an accident.

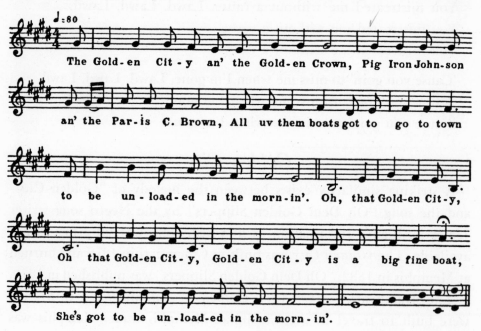

The Gold-en Cit-y an' the Gold-en Crown, Pig Iron John-son an' the Par-is C. Brown, All uv them boats got to go to town to be un-load-ed in the morn-in'. Oh, that Gold-en Cit-y, Oh that Gold-en Cit-y, Gold-en Cit-y is a big fine boat, She's got to be un-load-ed in the morn-in'.

Melody: Major scale.

Ferd Herold Blues

The *Ferd Herold,* a steel hull packet, was owned by Ferd Herold, a brewer, and Peter Hauptman, tobacco manufacturer, both of St. Louis. After operating for a time, in competition with the established lines, at a loss to the owners, the boat was sold to the Lee Line. She was finally dismantled and the hull was used for a barge.

Big boat's up the riv-uh an' she won't come down, Big boat's up the riv-uh an' she won't come down, Lawd, Lawd, I be-lieve to my soul that the boat's a-groun' Lawd, Lawd.

Melody: Tonic chord (minor) with 7th degree of natural minor scale.
Phrase groups of three.

When I come to town, Baby, what you want me to bring you back,
When I come to town, Baby, what you want me to bring you back,
    Lawd, Lawd,
I want a new pair uv shoes an' a Merry Widow hat, Lawd, Lawd.

Blow yo' whistle, captain, tell me the time uv day,
Blow yo' whistle, captain, tell me the time uv day, Lawd, Lawd,
I b'lieve it's time I'm eatin', fo' the mules done had their oats an' hay,
    Lawd, Lawd.

Evuh time I hear that big boat blow,
Evuh time I hear that big boat blow, Lawd, Lawd,
My mind rambles an' my feet are bound to go, Lawd, Lawd.

Ferd Herold been up the rivuh twenty days, an' she won't come down,
Ferd Herold been up the rivuh twenty days, an' she won't come down,
    Lawd, Lawd,
Low watuh's up the rivuh an' the boat has run agroun', Lawd, Lawd.

I'm Alabama Bound

"The Stack," "The Big Smoke," "Stack o' Dolluhs," "Bull of the Woods," and various other nicknames were invented by the Negroes for the packet *Stacker Lee*. This boat was of the famous Lee Line, established before the War Between the States, by Captain James Lee. Captain Lee was the father of four sons and two daughters, and boats were named for his children. One of the sons was Stacker Lee, but the steamboat bearing his name was not built until after his death.

The *Stacker Lee* was one of the largest packets afloat. She was capable of carrying an enormous cargo, and she was fleet. She was in the Cincinnati to Memphis trade, and she also operated from Memphis to St. Louis, and from Memphis to Vicksburg, alternating in these routes because of the stages of the rivers and the ice in winter.

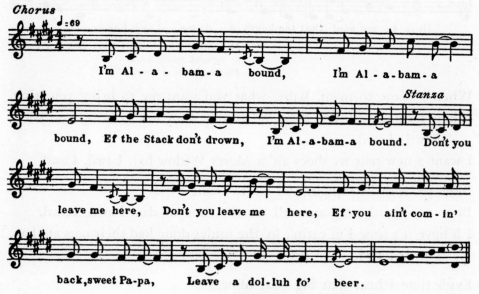

I'm Al - a - bam - a bound, I'm Al - a - bam - a bound, Ef the Stack don't drown, I'm Al - a - bam - a bound. Don't you leave me here, Don't you leave me here, Ef you ain't com - in' back, sweet Pa - pa, Leave a dol - luh fo' beer.

Melody: Major scale.
Musically, the chorus and verses are repetition except for the rhythmic fitting of the words.
Rondo form.

He's on the road somewheres,
He's on the road somewheres,
I've got a long tall easy ridin' Papa
On the road somewheres.

It'll be soon some mornin'
Or late some night,
He'll be knockin' at my do', sweet Papa,
Befo' daylight.

But blow yo' whistle, captain,
An' ring yo' bell,
Fo' the time the bullyin' Stack comes in town,
No woman kin tell.

Katie an' the Jim Lee Had a Race

The eight lines of this song are rich in background to anyone who understands the language of the river. It is one of the many rouster songs that tell the story of the rivalry between the *Kate Adams* and the *James Lee*. The *Kate Adams* mentioned here is the third boat of this name, known as the "Lovin' Kate." The "Jim Lee" of the famous Lee Line, was the second *James Lee*.

These two boats, beautiful side-wheelers, were both favorite packets, and for a time had overlapping trades in the Mississippi. The "Lovin' Kate," at this period, was in the Memphis-Arkansas City U.S. Mail Trade, and the *James Lee,* also a mail boat, traveled from Memphis to Friar's Point. This gave them many opportunities to match their speed and it was generally conceded that of the two, the *Kate Adams* was capable of a little better time.

A retired marine engineer, now living in the Ohio Valley, was striker engineer on the *James Lee* when she made her first trip, in 1898. He says, "If the *Kate Adams* had a good cargo of cotton we could pass her, and sometimes did. But when the boats were equally loaded, the *Adams* could go 'roun' the *Lee*."

There is no record of any formal race between these two boats, but the rousters will tell you that on one occasion the pilot of the *James Lee* ran into the bank, injuring his boat, to avoid giving victory in speed to the *Kate Adams*. The foundation for this story, no doubt, is the fact that during one of the many friendly contests between these two rivals, the tiller rope of the *James Lee* broke, and the boat struck the bank with such force that she was badly damaged, and had to be sent for repairs to the Marine Ways[7] in Paducah, on the Ohio River.

The emblem of victory in a race was a pair of mounted deer horns. After acquiring this trophy, the boat was allowed to keep it until she was forced to surrender it, after another race, to a successful rival.

In the days when the steamboat represented the height of fleetness in transportation, the privilege of carrying the United States mail was a coveted distinction. Passengers usually planned to board the mail boats, because they always stopped without being signaled, at the various landings, for the purpose of taking on or leaving mail.

The song was sung in a spirited tempo. The melody, built on four tones, suggests a rather rapid chant.

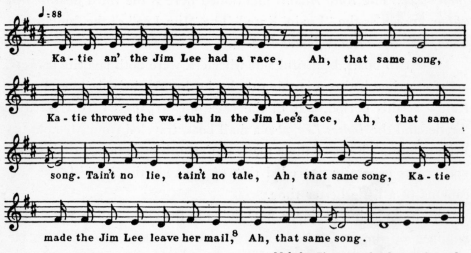

Ka-tie an' the Jim Lee had a race, Ah, that same song,

Ka-tie threwed the wa-tuh in the Jim Lee's face, Ah, that same

song. Tain't no lie, tain't no tale, Ah, that same song, Ka-tie

made the Jim Lee leave her mail,[8] Ah, that same song.

Melody: First tetrachord of major scale.

[7] The first Marine Ways on the lower Ohio were established at Smithland, Kentucky, by Watts, Given and Company, and were operated by horse power. In 1857 when the wharf boats

STEAMBOAT WHISTLE

I Am Waitin' on the Levee

The *Natchez* and the *Robert E. Lee* are associated in song and story. They were rivals in the New Orleans-Natchez trade during the heyday of the passenger packet, and on June 30, 1870, they made the famous race that is probably the most celebrated boat race in history. The run was from New Orleans to St. Louis.

Captain John W. Cannon of the *Lee,* a Kentuckian by birth, dismantled his boat for the contest and accepted no passengers or freight. Captain Thomas P. Leathers of the *Natchez,* also a Kentuckian, took passengers and freight as usual.

The bets on this trial of speed amounted to nearly two million dollars in America and Europe, and progress of the boats was reported by telegraph and cable to waiting crowds. The *Natchez* reached St. Louis nearly seven hours after the *Lee* had tied up. Consideration for the safety of his passengers had forced Captain Leathers to lay up for six hours in a fog.

Most of the bets in Europe were called off, but those in America were paid. It was generally conceded, even after the race, that under ordinary circumstances the running time of the two boats was about the same, with odds slightly in favor of the *Natchez.*

The *Robert E. Lee* was built in 1866 at Cincinnati; the *Natchez,* in 1869 at New Albany, Indiana.

---

and other river interests of this firm were moved to Paducah, Ed and Elijah Murray were engaged to build a set of steam operated ways. This plant was carried on under the supervision of the Murray Brothers until after the War Between the States, when Watts, Given and Company sold it to Samuel B. Hughes and J. W. McKnight of Paducah. The Ways are now owned and operated by the Ayer Lord Tie Company. Since its organization in 1857 this plant has been and is now of the largest capacity of any Ways on the Western Waters.

[8] In her effort to keep up with "Lovin' Kate" the *James Lee* overlooked some of her scheduled stops.

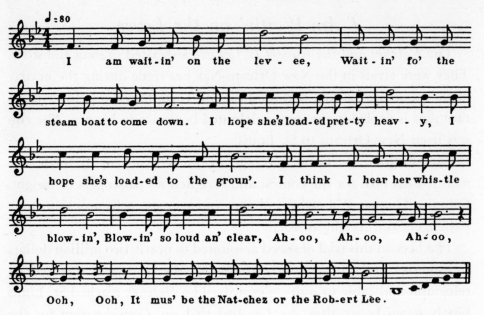

I am wait-in' on the lev-ee, Wait-in' fo' the steam boat to come down. I hope she's load-ed pret-ty heav-y, I hope she's load-ed to the groun'. I think I hear her whis-tle blow-in', Blow-in' so loud an' clear, Ah-oo, Ah-oo, Ah-oo, Ooh, Ooh, It mus' be the Nat-chez or the Rob-ert Lee.

Melody: Major scale—4th omitted.

4

Soundings

WHEN it is necessary to know the depth of the water at any point in the river, the test or sounding is made by dropping a 33-foot rope, to the end of which is fastened a pipe filled with lead. The pipe is about one and a half inches in diameter and twelve inches in length. A few inches of heavy chain are put into the pipe, and around this melted lead is poured. The weight of a lead is between six and ten pounds. The rope is fastened to a link of the chain that is allowed to extend past the length of the pipe. The length of the lead line is marked at four feet by a piece of white flannel woven into the rope, at six feet, by a piece of leather, at nine feet by a piece of red cloth; at Mark Twain there is a piece of leather split into two thongs, at Mark Three a piece of leather in three thongs, and at Mark Four there is a single leather strip with a round hole. These signals are recognized by the leadsman as the rope slips through his hands in the darkness.

The soundings are called out as the line drops. A depth less than Quarter Less Twain is given in feet. After Mark Four is reached the measurement is usually given as No Bottom.

There are two methods of taking soundings. If the length of the pipe at the end of the rope rests in a horizontal position on the ground of the river bed, the measurement is known as Laying Lead. If only the end of the pipe is allowed to touch the bottom the measurement is Standing Lead.

The report of the leadsman must reach the pilot quite a distance away. On large boats the messages are sometimes relayed by a man stationed between the leadsman and the pilothouse. The Negroes call this "passin' the word." In order to make themselves understood, often through wind and rain, the measurements are sung in a sustained chant, and each leadsman evolves his own tune and rhythm that he associates with the various depths.

One old Negro who used to take soundings or "heave the lead" on the Ohio gave this explanation of the prolonged tones, "You hold it out so the man who is passin' the word kin hear it mo' bettuh than if you cuts it off short."

The leadsmen realize the importance of their task. They enjoy the knowledge that their reports can cause such concern to the captain and the pilot. A Negro leadsman once said to the captain, "I laks you better than I do the pilot. I always gives you mo' watuh then I do him."

No darkie would ever confess to the crime of "Dry Leadin'," or reporting a depth not carefully measured. But it was probably on a night in winter that this song was first sung—a night so cold that it was not pleasant to draw up the line dripping with icy water:

> Captain, captain, don't you think I'm sly,
> Goin' to do my leadin' an' keep my lead line dry.

When a pilot "calls for the lead" he gives the command with a signal from the whistle or bell. Soundings are taken from either side of the boat, and when necessary from both sides. One signal from the pilothouse sends a leadsman to the starboard side, two signals to the larboard. The same signals from the pilothouse recall the leadsman from his post. The darkies say, "He blows you on, an' you has to stay out there till he blows you off."

Soundings are taken at the discretion of the pilot, when making a crossing, going through seldom used chutes, or at any time when there is doubt regarding the depth of the water. When a leadsman is at work the pilot expects to be informed of the depth of the channel about every hundred feet.

Throughout the leadsman's chanting, pilots listen hopefully for "No Bottom." To them this is the leadsman's sweetest song. When a boat can be kept in deep water the danger of going aground is avoided.

Quarter Less Twain ....ten and one-half feet
Mark Twain ....twelve feet (two fathoms)
Quarter Twain ....thirteen and one-half feet
Half Twain ....fifteen feet
Quarter Less Ta-ree (three) ....sixteen and one-half feet
Mark Ta-ree ....eighteen feet (three fathoms)
Quarter Ta-ree ....nineteen and one-half feet
Half Ta-ree ....twenty-one feet
Quarter Less Fo' ....twenty-two and one-half feet
Mark Fo' ....twenty-four feet (four fathoms)
    or
Deep Fo'[1]
No Bottom ....over twenty-four feet

Soundings at Memphis

It was on the Mississippi that I heard Soundings for the first time. That summer afternoon I was on the wharf at Memphis with a former officer of the third *Kate Adams*. He had arranged for an old leadsman to meet us there. We went out in a small boat and as the lead line dropped into the water the old Negro called out the measurements.

Later as he drew up the rope from the sparkling sunlit ripples his strong brown hands coiled it expertly, handling it with the care that should be given to something valuable and useful. Then he courteously repeated his chant more softly while I wrote down the melody given here.

[1] Some leadsmen use the measurement Deep Four instead of Mark Four. Deep Four indicates a depth slightly greater than four fathoms, or about twenty-five and a half feet instead of twenty-four or Mark Four.

Melody: Tonic chord (major); the D is an attempt to notate the characteristic slide.

Soundings from Uncle Mac

Old Mac Caldwell is proud of his long service as a leadsman. He told me, "I started out on the rivuh when I was seventeen year ole. A white man an' a black man togethuh learned me to lead. They learned me when I done been on the rivuh 'bout two year, an' I leaded till I quit. I leaded on the Ohio, an' the Mississippi, an' the Tennessee. The Tennessee's got the bes' bottom uv any rivuh in the country.

"Leadin' is the hardes' thing they is to learn on the rivuh; I mean it's the hardes' thing my people has to learn. They don't put black folks in the places the white folks is in on the boats—they got history fo' that I reckon—but some uv the white men I leaded fo' wuz always jes ez glad to see me ez if I wuz they brothuh. The white men I worked fo' is dead. Sometimes I stedy 'bout 'em all, an' the tears run out uv my eyes. Steamboatin' people always did think a lot uv each othuh. I nevuh had trouble with no white man on no boat I evuh worked on, an' I ain't nevuh throwed nobody ovuhboa'd aftuh dark."

Mac is eighty-two years old. When I asked him if he could show me how he used to lead, he said, "I kin wake up at midnight an' sing any uv them Marks. I ain't nevuh forgot the lead. The good Lord jes lef' that mind with me."

Uncle Mac lives in a small cottage in Paducah, Kentucky, on the Ohio River. It was here that he taught me his version of Soundings.

Melody: Tonic chord (major).

Soundings from Tee Collins

Another old leadsman is Tee Collins. When he sang for me he said, "I learned to lead by passin' the word. Then 'cause I always could holla pretty good, I started leadin'. The Marks is always the same, but evuhbody don't holla alike. Some don't holla ez good ez othuhs. They has different tunes. Leadin' sounds real lonesome at night."

Uncle Tee has "heaved the lead" on the Ohio, the Tennessee, and the Mississippi.

Quar - ter Less Ta - wain.

Mark   Ta - wain.

Quar - ter Ta - wain.

Ha - yaf Ta - wain.

Quar-ter Less Tha - ree.

Mark   Tha - ree.

Quar-ter   Tha - ree.

Ha - yaf   Tha - ree.

Quar - ter Less Fo - wer.

Mark   Fo - wer.

There is No   Bo - ot - tom.

Melody: Tonic chord (major).

5

Spirituals

IN ANY collection of songs of the Negro there will be many religious songs, or spirituals. This type of song is an expression of the religious feeling that is a definite part of the Negro's life, and we find it on the river as well as on land, wherever the Negro lives and reveals his thoughts, as he always does in singing.

In many of the spirituals of the rousters, the background of the river can be seen as clearly as in the secular songs. A great number of them are also labor songs, and in these the trotting rhythm, appropriate for work on the levee, is evident.

There are few of us perhaps who have not at some time in our lives dedicated some thoughts of regret to all of the innocent things that have been outlawed through the ages because of mistaken zeal for good. A collector of river songs will pay more than the usual tribute to this shrine. Among the older rousters we often come across the idea that certain tunes of the river should be definitely put aside as belonging to a period of worldly youth.

Of course there are some of the songs that we might not enjoy hearing, even though an appreciation of genuine things may give us a sturdy liking for uncensored versions. One old Negro, when asked to sing, said, "No, honey, God hears me speak. I don't know no rouster songs fittin' fo' a nice lady to write down."

However, it is not the touch of coarseness that we would expect to

find, and do find in some of the songs, that is the genesis of this inhibi-
tion, but apparently a conviction that the chances of a smooth voyage
in the next world are better if the "devilment songs" are "disremembered." One old man told me that many of the packet boat songs were
"reels an' jigs" and that now since he has "become a Christian" he
cannot sing them. The reels and jigs are "sinful songs." The "jump ups"
too are not always in good favor, as they are sometimes too closely
related to the jigs. Uncle Clabe Riley, an old Negro now blind, says,
"A 'jump up' is the kind uv song that comes right up in yo' head when
you're lonesome an' git to thinkin' about it."

I Come Up Out uv Egypt

After leaving the river Uncle Clabe "followed preachin'," and I had
trouble persuading him to sing. I had almost become discouraged, when
by accident I found him in just the right mood. One Sunday afternoon
I was near his house, and deciding to make one final effort, stopped to
see him. He had just returned from Church, and to my surprise he
was in an almost hilarious humor. He was wearing a frayed, stiff collar,
and a formal long-tailed coat that had found its way into his hands
after an unknown, but no doubt varied, past career of usefulness. His
singing this afternoon was unrestrained and animated. Several darkies
from next door came over to join in and to listen, and they all tried
to help me in my task of writing, by telling Clabe when to repeat, and
when to begin again after a pause, as he was unable to see my pencil,
trying, none too successfully, to keep pace with the singing. The difficulties of getting the songs on paper were a source of mirth to the
singers, and, when reading from my notes I made errors in repeating
words or tune, my mistakes were the occasion for much laughter and
slapping of knees. We were all in a gale of noisy good humor, and
Clabe, without realizing it, tapped his foot and even sang a song or
two that he probably would have "disremembered" in his more sober
moods.

A MINSTREL OF THE OHIO

A few days later a stooped, bent old Negro was leaning against a wall in the downtown district, holding out a tin cup. He held a heavy cane in one hand, and his head was bowed. Across his breast was a large soiled piece of cardboard on which were printed in rather zigzag letters the words, "I am blind." He looked properly friendless and forsaken. I had often seen him here before, but not until today did I recognize him. Remembering the boisterous gaiety of the past Sunday, I could not refrain from smiling now at the forlorn appearance Clabe managed to assume. I dropped a coin in the cup without speaking. I hoped the small piece of silver would serve as a penance for the smile.

Because "I Come Up Out uv Egypt" is a "Christian song," Clabe was willing to sing it; but he did not want to be misunderstood, so he explained, "Yes chile, this heah is a 'jump up' but hit ain't bad, even if them rousters did allus pat they foot when they sung it."

Melody: Major scale—4th omitted.

> When I wuz a preacher,
> I preached on many calls,
> Mourners down a-hollerin',
> Oh mercy, mercy, Lawd.
>
> The time I fought the battle,
> The time is past an' gone,
> I overtook the dragon
> An' carried the chillun along.

That's the Ba'm uv Gillud[1]
To make the wounded whole,
That's the Ba'm of Gillud,
To cure the sin-sick soul.

Red Sea

Clabe says that "Red Sea" was often sung just as the boat was loosened from the levee. He remembers that it was sung on the *Clyde*, the *Alabama*, and the *Kentucky*.

The *Kentucky*, known among the rousters as "Kentucky Belle," traveled on the Ohio, Tennessee, and Mississippi rivers. Her name was later changed to *Tennessee Belle*. On November 2, 1942, she was destroyed by fire, just below Natchez.

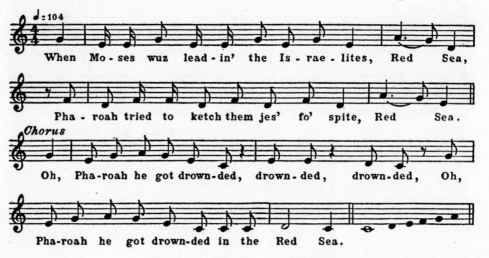

When Mo-ses wuz lead-in' the Is-rae-lites, Red Sea,
Pha-roah tried to ketch them jes' fo' spite, Red Sea.

Chorus

Oh, Pha-roah he got drown-ded, drown-ded, drown-ded, Oh,
Pha-roah he got drown-ded in the Red Sea.

Melody: First six tones of major scale.

I nevuh shall fo'git the day,
Red Sea,
When Jesus washed my sins away,
Red Sea.

[1] Balm of Gilead.

> I nevuh shall fo'git the day,
> Red Sea,
> When Jesus preached among the po',
> Red Sea.

Gabriel's Trumpet

Another "jump up" I learned from Clabe is "Gabriel's Trumpet." The first three lines marked "chorus" were sung at the beginning of the song. When the song was repeated, these lines were sung after one verse, and another time they were at the close. Uncle Clabe could not say what the usual way was.

Chorus ♩=96

Bap-tist, Bap-tist, is my name, I hope to live an' die the same, Oh Bap-tist num-bered in God.

Stanza

Ga-briel's trum-pet is the voice uv God, To wake up the mem-bers in the ole Church Yard, Oh Bap-tist num-bered in God.

Melody: Pentatonic scale.
Phrase groups of three.

> Ain't but one thing grieves my mind,
> My sister's gone to heaven an' lef' me behind,
> Oh Baptist, numbered in God.

> I'm goin' down to the new buryin' groun',
> Don't you hear my coughin' soun',
> Oh Baptist, numbered in God.

If I git drowned in the middle uv the sea,
Jesus Christ will surely waken me,
Oh Baptist, numbered in God.

Jesus Nevuh Come in the Mornin'

While I was sitting on the porch step of Berry Hubbard's cabin talking to him about the days when he "wuz steamboatin'," I realized anew how nearly vanished are the songs of that era. Berry is eighty years old, and he has "roustered" on most of the important Ohio River packets of his day. He said that since my last visit he had "talked to God" and had been instructed by him "not to sing none uv them sinful songs" for that would make him "in league with the devil." When he had finished singing the song given below he said, "This here is a sanctified song. They sing it when they git to shoutin'. When you're sanctified, evuhthing you do is right. You don't nevuh do nothin' wrong, an' evuhbody is always hoped up in Christ." This is the only kind of song Berry is willing to remember now.

Oh Jesus nevuh come in the mornin',
Neither in the heat uv the day, But come in the cool
uv the evenin' An' wash my sins away.

Melody: Tonic chord (minor).

Need not crave riches,
Neither dress so fine,
The robe that God A'mighty give you,
Outshine the radiant sun.

Go on down, Michael,
Go on down below,
Soun' you' trumpet, Gabul[2]
Time shall be no mo'.

Harvest field is ripenin',
Laborers is but few,
Git yo' garment ready,
Be a laborer too.

Lawd, I will die on the field uv battle,
Will die in the war,
Will die on the field uv battle,
Glory in my soul.

This Ole Worl' Ain't Goin' to Stan' Much Longer

Another old Negro was always willing to talk about the "package boats" and the days on the river, but he had this same determination not to join forces with the Evil One by singing reels and "rag downs." He said, "Yes, chile, a lot uv 'em does it, but when they does they ain't thinkin' uv the soul an' Christian things. After you 'fess religion you supposed to leave them things off. The Bible teaches that all them no-harm-things is a sin. When you come out frum the worl' you lay them things aside. We sung this here song in them days, but it's a song that makes the Sperit come to the body."

[2] Gabriel.

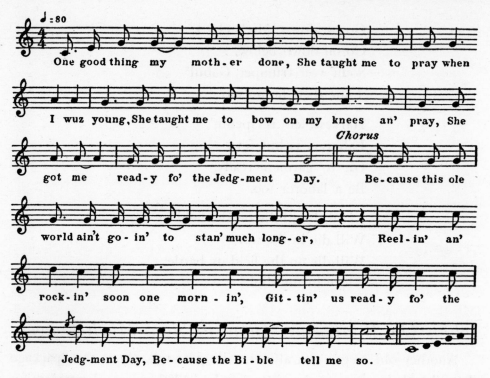

One good thing my moth-er done, She taught me to pray when I wuz young, She taught me to bow on my knees an' pray, She got me read-y fo' the Jedg-ment Day. *Chorus* Be-cause this ole world ain't go-in' to stan' much long-er, Reel-in' an' rock-in' soon one morn-in', Git-tin' us read-y fo' the Jedg-ment Day, Be-cause the Bi-ble tell me so.

Melody: Pentatonic scale.

God told Hezekiah, "You mus' die,"
He turned his face to the wall an' cried,
He cried, "Save me Jesus, save me now,
Let me stay until I change my mind.

"Step in Doctor, set yo' grip aside,
I don't need medicine, 'cause I'm sanctified,
I've got somethin' I'm not ashamed to tell,
I bought my tickets at the gates of Hell.

"Sound yo' trumpet, Gabriel, blow it hard,
Christ is comin' on the cloud,
I know my name is written on high,
An' my little soul ain't afraid to die.

"I don't need no pillow when I come to die,
Safe in Jesus an' I am satisfied,
I have been to Jordan an' been baptized,
So when Jesus come I kin rise an' fly."

Is Yo' Lamps Gone Out?

During the time that the river was still a busy thoroughfare, Susan was living in a town on the Ohio where large boats were constantly coming and going. She had worked for one family for years, and was a reliable and trusted servant, but the opportunity of "goin' on the rivuh" opened up such possibilities for adventure and chances to see different places and people that she became a chambermaid on one of the packets. Until river trade declined, she continued to work happily on various passenger boats that traveled on the Ohio, Tennessee, and Mississippi.

When her boat was in port taking on passengers or freight Susan would often come ashore to see her "white folks," and a little girl in the family was sometimes allowed to go with her "down to the boat." There were just four blocks to walk before reaching the river. The child would take Susan's kind brown hand before going down the steep levee and into the wharf boat where heavy freight was being handled. When they reached the white steamboat there were steps to climb, up to the boiler deck, and there one could look down over the rail and see the great wheel, quiet now, but still cool and dripping.

Sometimes during these happy mornings on the boat Susan would tie several pieces of string together, and fasten a tiny empty tin can to the end. The brand of snuff she used came in these diminutive containers, about one and a half inches high, and she could always manage to produce one when a toy was needed. It was a diverting game to lower the can over the rail as far as the string would permit, and sometimes it was possible to bring it up again full of water from the Ohio, far down below.

Years later when I was attempting to bring together some of the songs of these days of the river, it was natural for my thoughts to turn to Susan. The cottage in which she now lives is not far from a highway, but it is so hidden by thick shade that her chickens seldom stray away from the secluded doorstep. One summer afternoon I found Susan sitting in a "split bottom" chair under a large oak tree that spreads its branches over the entire cabin. She drew up a bucket of water from the well near the back door and I drank from a long-handled gourd dipper that hangs on a nail in the side of the house.

Susan's days of work are over, but her love for the big boats is unchanged. Many of the songs she remembers only in part, but she managed to recall "Is Yo' Lamps Gone Out?" which was sung on the *Joe Fowler* and the *Nisbet*.

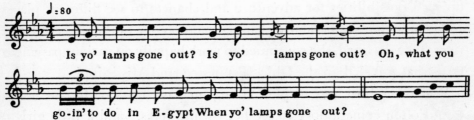

Is yo' lamps gone out? Is yo' lamps gone out? Oh, what you go-in' to do in E-gypt When yo' lamps gone out?

Melody: Pentatonic scale.

> If you git there
> Befo' I do,
> Oh, what you goin' to do in Egypt
> When yo' lamps gone out?
>
> The tallest tree
> In Paradise,
> Oh, what you goin' to do in Egypt
> When yo' lamps gone out?
>
> The Christians call it
> The Tree of Life,
> Oh, what you goin' to do in Egypt
> When yo' lamps gone out?
>
> Oh come, my Sister
> An' go with me,
> Oh, what you goin' to do in Egypt
> When yo' lamps gone out?

SUSAN AT THE WELL

I'll show you the Man
That set me free,
Oh, what you goin' to do in Egypt
When yo' lamps gone out?

Where Wuz You Las' Night?

"Where Wuz You Las' Night?" was taken down from the singing of Uncle Henry Johnson, eighty-nine years old. With coal-black skin and hair white as cotton, Uncle Henry is a picturesque figure from a day that is gone. It is to the still living "old fashioned darkies" of Uncle Henry's generation and to the surviving river men of the same time that we must look for a glimpse into the almost vanished period of the river's greatest glamour and prestige.

Sometimes, as many as seventy-five rousters would be needed on a packet to handle the freight at stopping points, and a trip often lasted for a month at a time. A special place for the rousters to sleep was not provided. They would often rest on the freight, or lie on the lower deck. In cold weather they liked to sleep under the boilers. This space was known among the rousters as "hog heaven," and it was also called "The St. Charles," the latter nickname originating, no doubt, from the St. Charles Hotels that were found at this time in almost every river town of importance.

Uncle Henry tells the story of a small pig that was given to a steamboat captain as a present. The rousters made a pet of it, and the animal finally attained a weight of three hundred seventy-four pounds, at which time, Henry says, the captain got rid of it because the hog "wuz gettin' heavy on its feet." During its sojourn on the boat the hog would seek a desirable place to rest, along with the rousters, and in cold weather it slept contentedly with a darkie on each side. Sometimes on severe winter nights there would be an argument among the Negroes over the privilege of this cozy arrangement, and the question would be settled only after a fight.

When the steamboat "wuz leavin' po't," according to Henry, "the rousters would be a-whoopin' an' a-hollerin', an' somebody would raise the song. Then they would sto' it like a pig, jes' lookin' fo' a place to rest."

The religious songs of the Negro are not set apart by him for use in church, or for special occasions only. As he works he often sings a "Christian song" that has a rhythm definite enough to give purpose to the monotony of his duties. In "Where Wuz You Las' Night?" we have a combination of a labor song and a spiritual. The tune, built on the tonic chord, has an animated swing, and the words suggest that the rouster's thoughts are divided between a pleasant dwelling upon the joys of the next world, and a disturbing recollection of the loud voices of the mate and captain—voices that keep him at work, and call him harshly from his dreams under the "bilers."

Chorus

Oh, where wuz you las' night? Where wuz you las' night? Where wuz you las' night? Un-der them bi-lers sleep-in'.

Stanza

I went in the val-ley, Lawd, I did-n't go to stay, Un-der them bi-lers sleep-in', My soul got hap-py, Lawd, I stayed all day, Un-der them bi-lers sleep-in'.

Melody: Tonic chord (major).
Rondo form.

The head mate hollered an' the captain squalled,
Under them bilers sleepin',
An' those niggers begun to go,
Under them bilers sleepin'.

I want to go to Heaven, Lawd, I want to go right,
Under them bilers sleepin'.
I want my garment neat an' nice,
Under them bilers sleepin'.

6

Songs of Meditation

VERY few of the roustabout songs do not have a rhythm that could be an accompaniment to manual labor; however, the slow tempo of some of them suggests that they were probably created and sung during less active moments than were usual on the levee when there was a cargo to handle.

Songs of meditation often have the repetition that is usual in all folk music. In the work songs this reiteration of lines served as an aid in the performance of the task at hand. In the more wistful songs, the repeating produces a soothing effect of relaxation, not at all unpleasant, even though it is often coupled with a melody that is weird and plaintive.

Ain't Got No Place to Lay My Head

Because the life of the Southern Negro is so simple, he is spared many of the fears that shadow those of us who are more dependent upon material possessions. He does not dread poverty as a probable menace, because poverty is to him the usual order, and the struggle against it he willingly and wisely leaves to the "white folks." However, there is one misfortune that to him represents all phases of financial loss, and that is "to be put out uv do's." It is interesting to notice how the living conditions and temperament of a people are reflected in their vocabulary and songs. "Ain't Got No Place To Lay My Head" is a mournful expression of a child-like race, defenseless and uncomprehending in the face of disaster. It was sung on the *Joe Fowler* and the *John S. Hopkins*.

Ain't got no place to lay my head, oh Ba - by,

Ain't got no place to lay my head, oh Ba - by,

Ain't got no place to lay my head.

Melody: First six tones of major scale.
Phrase groups of three.

Steamboat done put me out of do's, oh Baby,
Steamboat done put me out of do's, oh Baby,
Steamboat done put me out of do's.

Steamboat done lef' me an' gone, oh Baby,
Steamboat done lef' me an' gone, oh Baby,
Steamboat done lef' me an' gone.

Don' know what in this worl' I'm goin' to do, oh Baby,
Don' know what in this worl' I'm goin' to do, oh Baby,
Don' know what in this worl' I'm goin' to do.

Sweetheart's done quit me an' he's gone, oh Baby,
Sweetheart's done quit me an' he's gone, oh Baby,
Sweetheart's done quit me an' he's gone.

Out on the cold frozen groun', oh Baby,
Out on the cold frozen groun', oh Baby,
Out on the cold frozen groun'.

Ohio Rivuh, She's So Deep an' Wide

When an attempt is made to put a roustabout song down on paper,
we are often surprised at the ease with which the singers fit lines of

various lengths and accents to the same tune. This is especially evident in "Ohio River, She's So Deep an' Wide."

Uncle Mark, from whom this song of the river was obtained, lives in a cabin that overlooks the Ohio from a hill. To find him, the visitor must leave the highway and follow a dirt road cut deep with wagon ruts. This road soon becomes a narrow path that winds round large rocks and half-buried boulders, finally ending at a small grassy plateau that is Uncle Mark's front yard.

From Uncle Mark's porch today he sees heavily loaded coal barges and tow boats, instead of the graceful white packets of former years, but the Ohio itself has remained unchanged. Usually, an atmosphere of peace and calm strength is created by the river's deep beauty, but there are times when the Ohio seems possessed by an evil spirit and it becomes a surging yellow creature, aggressive and angry. Quantities of driftwood whirling in its ochre-colored current tell plainly a story of the river in a mood that is uncontrolled and menacing. Or again, still under the same terrible enchantment, it will resemble a wide clay-colored sea. At such times, the apparent quiet of its surface is not to be trusted, for it is rising steadily. Familiar landmarks along the banks gradually disappear as the river grows broader. The Ohio has become hungry and ungovernable, indifferent to the havoc caused by its own silent, relentless power. Until this spell is broken we look in vain for the river's lost graciousness, and we wait helplessly for a return of the gentle green serenity that we know and love.

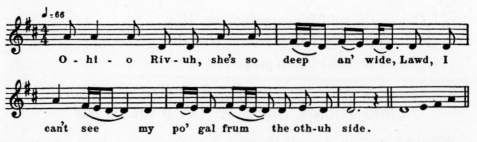

O-hi-o Riv-uh, she's so deep an' wide, Lawd, I
can't see my po' gal frum the oth-uh side.

Melody: Four tones of major scale—1st, 2d, 3rd, and 5th.

I'm goin' to rivuh, take my seat an' sit down,
Ef the blues overtake me, I'll jump in the rivuh an' drown.

I've got the blues, I've got the blues,
Lawd, I ain't got the heart to cry.

Uphead an' Scatter, Boys

It was from Aunt Belle Edmunds that I learned "Uphead an' Scatter, Boys." She was sitting on her porch fanning when I stopped to see her. I had been forced to make inquiries to find her. Since my last visit the Ohio, wider than usual, had sent "back water" over the floor of Aunt Belle's house. In speaking of her forced change of residence she said, "Yes, baby, the rivuh done run me out."

Several small Negro children on the sidewalk stopped playing to stare at the visitor. Aunt Belle sent one of them into the house for a can of snuff. I welcomed this opportunity to become enlightened regarding the pleasures of "dippin' snuff." It is good after eating, to settle the stomach, it seems. I also learned that "white folks likes they snuff too, but nobody knows it; they does it so sly."

Aunt Belle, eighty-six years old, was for over twenty years a chambermaid on the Fowler boats, in addition to long services on other Ohio packets. She can recall only snatches of the tunes she used to hear. She told me, "No, I can't write nothin' down, an' I can't read. Sometimes when I'm settin' here by myself, I think uv them songs, but then they leave me." She remembers that the rousters often sang at night, and when handling a cargo, according to Aunt Belle, "it seemed lak it done 'em good to be a-singin'."

For a picture of Aunt Belle I helped her down from the shady porch and moved her chair into the sun. The camera was open and ready, when we were delayed by the plaintive announcement, "Wait, chile, my teeth ain't in."

After singing the following song Aunt Belle said, "I ain't tried to sing none o' them songs fo' ovuh thirty years, but I allus remember that one, 'cause hits so true."

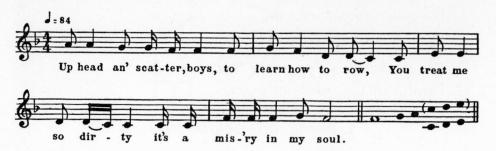

Up head an' scat-ter, boys, to learn how to row, You treat me
so dir - ty it's a mis-'ry in my soul.

Melody: Major scale—4th omitted.

When I had money, I had frien's all aroun',
But now I've no money, no frien' can be foun'.

I'm goin' to tell my Mammy when I go home,
You treat me so dirty, it's a mis'ry in my soul.

7

Love Songs

SONGS of love are found in the folk music of every nation and people. In this volume the songs have been considered primarily for their association with the river and the packet boats, and many classified in other groups are also love songs. The river roustabout was not lacking in sentiment.

A long journey always means separation, and for every voyage there were sweethearts left behind. When the darkies were ready to start on a trip there was one farewell message called out so invariably that it was familiar to everyone who frequented the wharves and levees. The Negroes would shout, "Ef you see my Baby, tell her I've gone on up."

Alberta, Let Yo' Hair Hang Low

It was late in the afternoon when I reached the street on which Uncle Gabriel Hester lived. Perhaps it should be called a wide lane. Street and sidewalk were one, and the path curved informally around a large oak tree. I chose my steps through empty tin cans, friendly panting dogs, and kinky-haired children, brown skinned and half clad. Darkies sat fanning on small porches, and some of them directed me to Uncle Gabe's house. He was not at home but was expected back at any minute, I was told, as this was the time he always fed the hog. I was encouraged to wait for him, as his wife replied to my inquiries, "Bless the Lawd, honey, he don't nevuh mind singin', an' he jes' loves to play on the box." When Uncle Gabe returned, he was pushing a little two-wheeled cart, filled with cantaloupe rinds and other garbage that he had been collecting for his pig, whose pen was a short distance from the door.

A few minutes later, the old man had obligingly got out his "box," and as he touched the guitar strings with gifted, untrained fingers, he sang the lovely melody of "Alberta, Let Yo' Hair Hang Low."

Knowing that Uncle Gabe had been a rouster in his youth, I questioned him about the years he had spent "steamboatin'." He told me that when a boat did an especially large freight business, she was known as the "Workhouse." This nickname, he explained, was given to any packet that was usually "draggin' her guards" from a heavy load.

Gabe said the rousters always sang "when they wuz a-wukin'," and he remembered how the passengers liked to hear singing in the evenings and would drop coins down from the upper decks when music came up to them from below. There were songs again when the rousters were gathered on the bow of the boat as she was going into port, and he recalled the crowds that were always waiting on the levee as the packet tied up.

By this time a few coal oil lamps had been lighted in neighboring houses, and soft voices could be heard from other porches. In the early dark, there was something wistful and unreal about this narrow, peaceful street, and it was with a strange reluctance that I walked back toward my own familiar world of concrete sidewalks and electric lights.

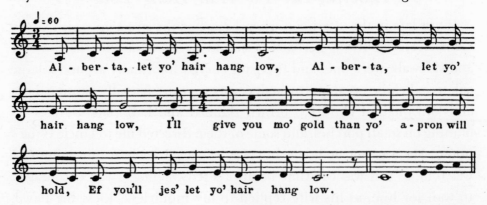

Al - ber - ta, let yo' hair hang low, Al - ber - ta, let yo'
hair hang low, I'll give you mo' gold than yo' a - pron will
hold, Ef you'll jes' let yo' hair hang low.

Melody: The opening measure, built of A and C suggests the minor mode, but following measures definitely imply the pentatonic scale, centering on C.

Alberta, what's on yo' mind?
Alberta, what's on yo' mind?
You keep me worried, you keep me bothered, all the time.
Alberta, what's on yo' mind?

Alberta, don't you treat me unkind,
Alberta, don't you treat me unkind,
'Cause I'm worried, 'cause I'm bothered, all the time.
Alberta, don't you treat me unkind.

Come On, My Pink, an' Tell Me What You Think

To reach Uncle Hal Williams' house, I climbed a steep trail over a hill thickly wooded with dogwood and wild plum. From his porch Uncle Hal can see far down the river, and the cardinals and blue birds live in his trees undisturbed.

The life lived today by some of these minstrels of the Ohio, who for so many years long ago "followed the river" is an existence that is, perhaps, as nearly ideal as one should desire in this era of unrest. Their cabins, as a rule, are in a quiet place not far from the river that was for so long a part of their lives, and they are sustained by the irresponsible childlike nature that is characteristic of the Negro race. Careless, carefree, and gentle, now that their strenuous days of work are over, they remember the busy past and are untroubled by the future.

In taking down "Come on, My Pink" and "Careless Love" the performance had to halt temporarily because a pet chicken had joined us as we sat on the porch. Uncle Hal's wife, Minerva, explained that the chicken was "mad" at her today because she had forgotten to leave the door open the night before, and the chicken had "done had to sleep outdo's."

♩ = 69

Come on, my Pink, an' tell me what you think, You're a

long time mak-in' up yo' mind. You tole mo' lies than there's

stars in the skies, An' yo' heart ain't no mo' mine, Yo' heart ain't

no mo' mine, Yo' heart ain't no mo' mine.

Melody: First six tones of major scale.
Phrase groups of three.

But late last night when my Baby come home,
I heard a mighty knockin' at the do',
I stepped across the flo' in my stockin' feet,
Baby, don't you knock no mo',
Baby, don't you knock no mo',
Baby, don't you knock no mo'.

Some ole boy in this town,
I wisht he wuz dead an' gone,
I'd drag that razor across his throat,
My Baby'd pay my fine,
My Baby'd pay my fine,
My Baby'd pay my fine.

Oh, hand me down my ole valise,
An' all my dirty clothes,
An' ef my Baby calls fo' me,
Jes' tell her I stepped out do's.
Go tell her I stepped out do's.
Go tell her I stepped out do's.

Oh, yonder comes the ole steamboat,

Sixteen barges long,

An' ef my Baby calls fo' me,

Jes' tell her I'm dead an' gone,

Oh, tell her I'm dead an' gone,

Oh, tell her I'm dead an' gone.

Careless Love

"Careless Love" is associated with the packet, *Dick Fowler,* which traveled only on the Ohio River. She was built for speed and made two daily trips to Cairo from Paducah.

Love, oh love, oh care-less love, Love, oh love, oh care-less love, You can't love no one, an' you can't love no two, Jes' love the one that say love you.

Melody: One of the few roustabout songs built on a complete major scale.
Ternary form—last two measures repetition of first two measures.

Ef I nevuh see you no mo',

Ef I nevuh see you no mo',

Ef I nevuh, nevuh see you no mo',

Wash the foot steps roun' yo' do'.

My Mamma tol' me, my Papa too,

My Mamma tol' me, my Papa too,

My Mamma tol' me, my Papa tol' me too,

Don't let no one make a fool uv you.

It killed my Mamma an' my Papa too,
It killed my Mamma an' my Papa too,
It killed my Papa, killed my Mamma too,
See what careless love will do.

Come, Love, Come, the Boat Lies Low

The following song was sung by Cliff, one hot summer afternoon, while he rested a few minutes from working in a small vegetable garden near his door. His cottage is on a bluff that overlooks the Ohio just at the point where it meets the Tennessee in rapid current.

There is a slight difference in the color of these two rivers, and as far as the eye can see they seem to flow side by side in the same channel, without blending. A distinct line of division is visible for a distance of several miles, as if the Tennessee were reluctant to give up its own identity.

A fallen tree at the back of the garden made a convenient seat for the visitor, but Cliff declined an invitation to sit on the other end of the log, and remained standing respectfully throughout the repetitions needed for the words and tune to be written down, sometimes wiping his forehead with a large colored handkerchief, and fanning with a tattered, broad-brimmed straw hat.

Cliff cannot remember just when he first heard this song, but says, "It wuz near 'bout sixty year' ago, I reckon."

Courtesy of W. L. Beasley, Jr.

"COME, LOVE, COME, THE BOAT LIES LOW"

Come, love, come, an' go with me, I'll take you down a-bout Ten-nes-see. O-pen up the win-dow, oh love do, Lis-ten to the mu-sic I'm play-in' fo' you. Come, love, come, the boat lies low, Lies high an' dry on the O-hi-o.

Chorus

Melody: First six tones of major scale.

Come, love, come, an' go with me
I'll take you down about Tennessee.
Next time I come be ready to go,
Floatin' down the rivuh on the Ole Ben Joe.

8

Dance Songs

THERE has always been a close connection between folk songs and dancing. Among people whose songs are usually somber, the dances are frequently animated and gay, as if the bodily movements provided a needed release from grief. The Negro dances are gay and carefree. Usually, the primary rhythm can be given with patting feet or clapping hands. Often the feet pat a beat, and at the same time, a syncopation is clapped, or a movement of the swaying body will emphasize an unexpected accent.

The words "jazz" and "ragtime" are generally accepted as including this strange feeling for rhythm that is such a vital part of all Negro music. No doubt the familiar "juba" was at one time the African "Guioba." It is possible that the Negro songs known as "Coonjines" originally referred to the old African dance, the "Coonjai." But to the "steamboat nigger" the Coonjine is the combination song and dance that is associated with handling freight. The "plank walk" springs under a heavy weight, or even under the lighter step of the rouster when he trots back again empty handed for more freight. To avoid jarring, the feet are dragged along the stage plank, accompanied by a song that takes its rhythm from the shuffling feet and swaying shoulders.

Possibly this levee dance step and the name "Coonjine" that describe it were inspired by the way a coon makes his way along the limb of a tree, steadying himself by keeping one foot safely on the limb, while he "coons along" with the other three.

Rowdy Soul

One day I stopped by to see Aunt Laura Bishop. She was sitting under a tree in her front yard, "piecin' a quilt" with bright colored squares of percale and calico. Fortunately for me, she was in a communicative mood.

It is possible to persuade Aunt Laura to talk about the Coonjine songs. She is more tolerant about them than many of the old Negroes, but she always makes it clear that she realizes that "dancin' an' singin' them reels" is a rather questionable business.

Laura was a maid on the Ohio and Tennessee river boats, and she told me how she used to watch the rousters dance. She said, "Yes, honey, they wuz reels, but they sounded good. They didn't mean no harm, an' they wuz so purty I stedy 'bout 'em now, lots uv times when I'm a-settin' heah by myself. It kep' them rousters joyful all the time, an' it hepped 'em to turn off they work. They'd be jes' rockin' an' laughin' an' singin'. They had a kind uv rock they'd swing theyselves in. Fust they'd start in a-singin' then when one uv 'em got up an' shuck his se'f they'd all jine in an' dance.

"Lawd, no, chile, I can't show you how they done it; I belongs to the Church; but I used to watch them boys. One time the Cap'm says to me, 'Laura I bet you been a-dancin',' an' I says to him, 'No suh! I ain't.' " She smiled and lowered her voice, "But chile, sposin' I had a-danced—what uv it?"

The rousters could work and coonjine to most of their songs, but some of them were more popular than others for dancing. "Rowdy Soul" seems to have been a favorite, probably because of its strong rhythm.

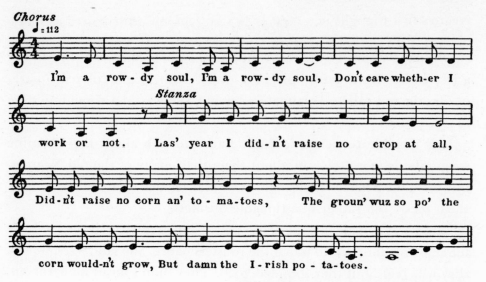

I'm a row-dy soul, I'm a row-dy soul, Don't care wheth-er I work or not. Las' year I did-n't raise no crop at all, Did-n't raise no corn an' to-ma-toes, The groun' wuz so po' the corn would-n't grow, But damn the I-rish po-ta-toes.

Melody: Natural minor scale in key of A. The tones are the same as the pentatonic scale, centering on C, but tonality is definitely A minor. Rondo form.

When I git my new house done,
An' build my chimley higher,
So the dirt dobbers[1] will quit flyin' roun',
An' put me out my fire.

I took my gal to the party, oh,
An' I didn't say nothin' 'bout it,
I ain't no hand to raise no row,
But I'm Hell when I git started.

Uncle Bud

Whenever a rouster had enough money to buy the kind of clothes he liked best, he would select a checked shirt and "bell bottom pants" of brown or blue jeans. A small pocket just below the belt was the ideal place for the rouster's favorite weapon—a bone-handled knife. The

[1] Yellow jackets or wasps.

Negro's first thought in a fight is of a knife. One white-haired narrator of river stories says, "There ain't nothin' worse than a half drunk nigger with a knife in his hand." The kind of knife preferred by the rouster had a blade that could be released by a spring from a pressure on the handle, so that it was ready for use by the time it could be drawn from the pocket. This weapon was sometimes carried in the sleeve for greater convenience, with the blade open, ready for immediate action.

In moments of relaxation the Negroes would play with these keen blades, and in sport they would make savage and ferocious lunges at their companions, missing the throat by a few safe inches. Sometimes when whiskey was plentiful and excitement high, these playful sparrings would change to reality, and too often tragic and unpleasant sights could be seen on the river bank.

In one river town the Blue Goose Saloon on the levee was a favorite meeting place, and a few of the old rousters can still remember how they used to dance there. The dancing was accompanied by singing, hand-clapping and stamping, one Negro at a time being in the center of a ring, doing a sort of solo dance, except when he would suddenly catch a near-by companion for a violent whirl or turn. The words and tune for the dance songs were not as important as the rhythm. Often the words seem entirely meaningless. Sometimes the name or nickname of an unmerciful mate, who was feared by the rousters, would be worked into a kind of singsong, or perhaps the name of the local chief of police would be given this distinction, combined with some rhythmic nonsense syllables punctuated with handclaps.

One old rouster known as "General Thomas," when questioned about the almost forgotten Blue Goose Saloon, smiled and gave us an account of how he "broke" all the rousters present with the aid of a pair of "hosses" that always fell into sevens and elevens. Later, when most of the crew were ashore in Evansville, "foolin' with women" he "cleaned up about ten dolluhs mo' frum some little green niggers what thought they knowed how to gamble."

When I asked for some description of the dancing of those days, General got up rather shakily from the log on which he had been sitting, and in spite of his seventy-six years and stooped shoulders, he was able to give us a good idea of the juba and the jig, all the while clapping his hands and singing:

> Juba this an' juba that,
> Juba killed the yellow cat.
> Do na ha juba,
> Do na ha juba.

After this exertion he dropped down heavily on the log and his breath came rapidly. But still smiling he said, "I used to make as much as ten dolluhs in a few minutes in Mr. Red Johnson's saloon dancin' the juba fo' the white folks, but that wuz a long time ago, them days."

From General I learned "Uncle Bud," which had been sung on the *Peters Lee.*

Oh, Uncle Bud go-in' down the road, Haul-in' wo-men by the wag-on load. Uncle Bud, Un-cle Bud, Un-cle Bud, Bud, Dog-gone it, Un-cle Bud.

Melody: Pentatonic scale—2d omitted.

> Up he slipped an' down he fell,
> Mouth fell open like a mussel shell.

> He passed by here, an' sweepin' low,
> Forgot his bottle an' overcoat.

> Some of these mornin's, it won't be long,
> I'll leave this town blowin' my horn.

Way down yonder where I come frum,
Feed them niggers off hard, parched corn.

Growed so tall, growed so fat,
Swelled up big, couldn't wear a hat.

Some folks say Uncle Bud wuzn't aroun',
It's a goddam lie, he's leavin' town.

Some folks say Uncle Bud wuz dead,
It's a goddam lie, he ought to be in bed.

Worked in the summer an' all the fall,
Now winter caught me in blue overalls.

Take Yo' Time

We are indebted for "Take Yo' Time" to two old Negro men who were sitting on an Ohio River levee, one hot July morning. They located Uncle Mark Hamilton, whose memory for river songs was known to his friends, and the three of them, ragged, casual, and good natured, all sang together.

The sun on the levee was hot, so we used this as an excuse to seek a more secluded place on a side street, where our group would be less conspicuous. We found an empty warehouse, and I sat on the doorstep, the singers on a railing that was a part of the entrance. While we were there, darkies were the only passers-by. As the singing got underway so many of them stopped to listen that we soon had a puzzled, wide-eyed audience standing on the sidewalk.

I have been told at various times by friends who are familiar with the roustabout as a type, that I should not be surprised if some of the river songs, when I heard them, were not just as the Negroes often sang them. Other friends, with something of the same idea in mind, seemed trying to prepare me for the danger of unexpurgated versions coming to my ears by accident. I had forgotten these tactful warnings until this morning. I was reminded of them first when the singers, after starting a line, hesitated and whispered together. Again a verse was begun and left unfinished. I tried to encourage them to go on with the song, but after another whispered consultation, Uncle Mark said, "No, lady, they wouldn't nobody but jes' don't-care people lak to hear them words."

I realized that a censorship was being exercised, but as the singing continued my interest in what I was hearing prevented speculation over possible omissions. "Take Yo' Time," originally a dance song, is given here just as it was sung.

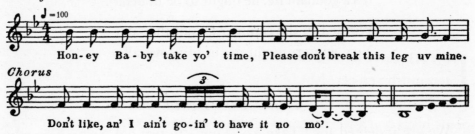

Hon-ey Ba-by take yo' time, Please don't break this leg uv mine.

Chorus

Don't like, an' I ain't go-in' to have it no mo'.

Melody: Major scale—2d and 7th omitted.

I'm going down the rivuh floatin' on a log,
See that cabin, cock it on a frog.

Mamma, Mamma, look at Sam,
Eatin' up the meat, soppin' the pan.

Oh, Mamma went to beatin' an' bangin' on Sam,
He kep' on eatin' like he didn't give a damn.

Say, Mamma, Mamma, look at Sis,
Down in the back yard doin' that twist.

Mamma says, "Come in the house, you dirty little wench,
You ought to be down on the Mourner's Bench."

Evuh time I go to town,
Somebody runs me roun' an' roun'.

Run me in my Baby's do',
You nevuh git a chance to run me no mo'.

9

Songs of Lawlessness

IN THE early days of the steamboat, human life was not held in any too much respect. Not infrequently a rouster would disappear, and any question asked regarding his fate caused embarrassment to no one. Some boats had a worse reputation than others for this kind of disorder. It was said of one Ohio packet that a Negro was killed aboard her every trip.

It was not just among the Negroes that fighting was more or less the usual thing. There was a rowdy type of white man of a low class who prided himself on his reputation for disgraceful behavior. The recognized bully felt himself a rather exalted person, second in importance only to the man who could "lay him down."

This may have been a survival of the days before the steamboat, when any kind of travel was hazardous. At this time men who were familiar with the ways of the river and the perils of a journey leased themselves out as guides to travelers. Any guide who was not bold and venturesome was in the wrong business, but the desperados of the flatboat days, who boasted that they were "half horse and half alligator," though a well-known type on the river, can hardly be said to have contributed anything worthwhile to the development of the Ohio Valley, even in those rugged times.

Stacker Lee No. 1

There are many Stacker Lee songs. Some of them can be connected with the packet boat; others center around the personality of a lawless character who was known and feared along the Ohio until a conviction for murder put an end to his career about forty years ago.

Stack-er Lee is look-in' fo' the Bul-ly, The Bul-ly can't be found, Now we're go-in' to walk the lev-ee roun', roun', Go-in' to walk the lev-ee roun', I'm look-in' fo' the Bul-ly uv yo' town. I'm look-in' fo' the Bul-ly, The Bul-ly mus' be found, I'm look-in' fo' the Bul-ly boys, To lay the bod-y down, I'm look-in' fo' the Bul-ly uv yo' town.

Melody: Major scale—2d and 7th omitted.
An example of the rare occurrence of triple
time among the rouster songs.

Stacker Lee No. 2

Among the Negroes there exist characters, either real or imaginary, that hold a firm place in Negro legend and song. These personalities have not always attained their prominence through good qualities.

There seems to be no doubt that a rouster by the name of Stacker

Lee really existed, but there are many conflicting stories about his life. Some of the Negroes say that his mother was for many years a chamber-maid on the Lee boats; others will tell you that he was born while his mother was a cook on board the *Stacker Lee*. The first theory seems more plausible because many of the Negroes place the crime so well known in Negro song at a date before the packet *Stacker Lee* was built.

Billy Lions, or sometimes Billy Galion, is the man Stacker Lee is supposed to have killed, and there seems no doubt that a Stetson hat had an important place in the affair.

The Stacker Lee song given below was sung by an old Negro named Fred Lee. He helps us to date the unfortunate story by asserting that he and the rouster Stacker Lee once spent the night in jail together. They were arrested in a saloon fight and put in the same cell. Fred still recalls the incident with apparent satisfaction.

The old darkies today speak affectionately of the families in which they or their parents were slaves. There is an amusing vagueness in the words they select to explain this relationship. Some times they speak of the "white folks" they "belonged to," but as often they will tell you of the family they "wuz kin to" or perhaps "related to." Fred told me that his grandfather had belonged to the Lee family. He added with pride, "Yes'm, it wuz the Lees that owned all them big boats."

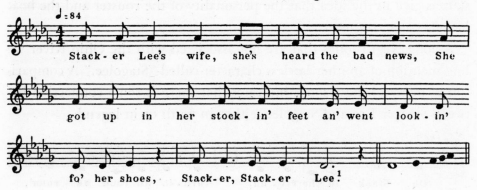

Stack-er Lee's wife, she's heard the bad news, She got up in her stock-in' feet an' went look-in' fo' her shoes, Stack-er, Stack-er Lee.[1]

Melody: First five tones of major scale.
Phrase groups of three.

[1] This line is also sung: "I wonder what Stacker Lee has done?"

Billy the Lion said, "Stacker Lee please don't take my life,
I have two children an' a lovin' little wife,"
Stacker, Stacker Lee.

"What do I care fo' yo' children, what do I care fo' yo' wife,
You taken my new Stetson hat, an' I'm goin' to take yo' life,"
Stacker, Stacker Lee.

Stacker Lee's wife said, "Stacker Lee ain't no need o' that,
I could uv bought you two dozen hats,"
Stacker, Stacker Lee.

You may go to Cairo, you may tip yo' hat,
You may walk up an' down the street, but the sheriff'll bring you back.
Stacker, Stacker Lee.

Stacker Lee's Mamma said, "Stacker Lee wuz the wurst she evuh nursed,
Stacker Lee wuz a bad boy, he wuz a bully frum his birth,"
Stacker, Stacker Lee.

Stacker Lee No. 3

In the song given as "Stacker Lee No. 3" the "Stack" mentioned in the first couplet seems to refer to the steamboat. The second and third stanzas give us the idea that the personality of the rouster and the boat have become confused.

Among Negro songs that are not associated with the Ohio River we find mention of another lawless character called "Stagolee." A comparison of many of these songs indicates that there is some connection between Stacker Lee and Stagolee, either in truth or in legend.

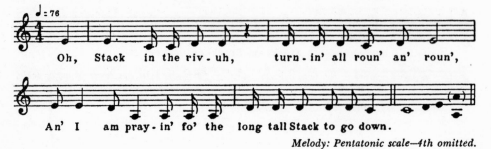

Oh, Stack in the riv-uh, turn-in' all roun' an' roun',
An' I am pray-in' fo' the long tall Stack to go down.

Melody: Pentatonic scale—4th omitted.

When the women hollerin' "Oh Mr. Stacker Lee,
Have taken my husban', an' made a trip fo' me."

Oh, Stack has got ways jes' lak a natural man,
He'll steal yo' woman, an' in the woods he'll lan'.

My Mother wuz a seamster, learn't me how to sew,
She learn't me how to Ball the Jack an' nevuh touch the flo'.

I don't want no woman to carry me roun' an' roun',
Jes' want some brown Baby to bounce me up an' down.

Been All Aroun' the Whole Roun' Worl'

When I asked one old Negro about the lawlessness among the rousters
he said, "Some people's got to be drove to do, an' they's always somebody
wantin' to be bulldozin'. Sometimes the captain uv the watch wuz worse
than the mate. They wuz mighty bad about fightin'. They'd be gamblin'
an' git into arguments. Then they'd be killin's. Many a one wuz killed
an' knocked ovuhbo'd an' nobody knowed nothin' 'bout it. Sometimes
they'd have a box made an' bury 'em on the sho'. The Good Lawd done
destroyed them things 'cause they wuz so bad."

The Negroes were not supposed to carry weapons but they often
managed to do it. On some of the boats the mate required the rousters
to line up after leaving the shore and throw their pistols and knives overboard.

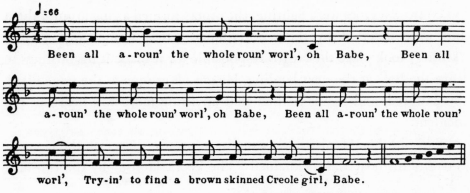

Been all a-roun' the whole roun' worl', oh Babe, Been all
a-roun' the whole roun' worl', oh Babe, Been all a-roun' the whole roun'
worl', Try-in' to find a brown skinned Creole girl, Babe.

*Melody: Major scale—6th omitted, with unique
use of the leading tone.*

Big Joe Fowler's roun' the ben', oh Babe,
Big Joe Fowler's roun' the ben', oh Babe,
Big Joe Fowler's roun' the ben',
She ain't doin' nothin' but killin' good men,[2] Babe.

I know somethin' you don't know, oh Babe,
I know somethin' you don't know, oh Babe,
I know somethin' you don't know,
You can't dodge my forty-fo', Babe.

I kin tote cotton an' I kin sort seed, oh Babe,
I kin tote cotton an' I kin sort seed, oh Babe,
I kin tote cotton an' I kin sort seed,
Give my family all they need, Babe.

Evuh since I killed a man, oh Babe,
Evuh since I killed a man, oh Babe,
Evuh since I killed a man,
Skippin' an' dodgin' right through the land, Babe.

Early in the Mornin'

Usually, any lines in the songs that describe arrests and sojourns in "the big jail" are reflections of the Negro's life on shore rather than on the river. There were disturbances aplenty on the river, but most of them were settled before the trip was over, without calling on the Law. When two Negroes were fighting, the others formed a ring around them and were diverted by the entertainment. If a serious injury or a "killin'" took place the Negro responsible for it made it his business to leave the boat at the next landing. He got off as soon as the stage plank was lowered, and it was seldom that anything more was heard of the incident.

"Early in the Mornin'" was sung by a former rouster on the *General Wood*. This boat was nicknamed "The Work House" by the rousters.

[2] This line refers to the strenuous work of the roustabouts.

Courtesy of Captain Frederick Way, Jr.

THE GENERAL WOOD

KNOWN AMONG THE ROUSTERS AS THE "WORKHOUSE"

Ear - ly   in   the morn - in'   jes' a - bout the break uv day, You ought to see me grab my pil - low, Where my good gal used to lay. I'm goin' up the riv - uh be - fo' long, I know you're goin' to miss me when I'm gone.

Melody: Tonic chord (major) with added 6th.
Chorus in three measure phrases.
Rondo form.

I'm gittin' so tired uv yo' low down dirty ways,
An' I'm goin' to leave you 'bout the break uv day.

I woke up this mornin' 'bout half past fo',
I foun' my good gal a-knockin' on the do'.

Goin' down the stream, comin' up the slough,
There ain't but one gal in town that I b'lieve is true.

If I had a-listened to what my Mammy said,
I could have been a-sleepin' on my Mammy's bed.

Kep' on goin', thought I wuz a man,
Kep' on goin' till in the big rock jail I lan'.

Devil

The rousters, except when singing of a packet, usually express their feelings in a song that is more personal than the true ballad. An exception to this general rule is the song "Devil," that grew up around an event which seems to have made a vivid impression upon the minds of the Negroes.

In a small Kentucky hamlet on the Ohio I stopped at a farmhouse to make inquiries about Uncle Joe Withers, who could often be found there doing odd jobs about the place. I was directed to the barn, where at that moment Joe was feeding the mules. As I walked out through a field of yellow Black-eyed Susans I wondered what success I would have in persuading Joe to sing some of the songs of his roustabout days. At first he hesitated, saying that he "disremembered all o' them songs," but he was finally induced to begin. Hoping to find some shade and a breeze outside the barn, we sat down on the ground under a tree. It was in this quiet pasture that Uncle Joe sang this version of "Devil." He told me that he had learned the song when he "wuz steamboatin' " and that it was well known among the rousters. Many versions of it contain lines that are not suitable for publication.

George Winston, known among his associates as Devil, began life as a cabin boy on the Mississippi. He was later an Ohio River rouster on packets going in and out of Paducah, Kentucky. His career of reckless lawlessness culminated when he was thirty-two years old, in the vicious murder of Vinie Stubblefield, his sweetheart. The brutal nature of this crime and the expiation of it seemed to grip the imagination of the Negroes of the time, and this ballad grew up around the event. The arrest and trial of Devil Winston followed the usual legal course, but feeling ran so high against him and there was such intense excitement among the Negroes of Paducah, where the crime was committed, that the exact hour of the execution was kept a secret, and it was deemed wise by the police to forbid, for the time being, the singing of this song.

The murdered Negress was said to have been half-witted and repulsive-looking. She had made several efforts to sever her relationship with Winston, and this was the indirect cause of her death. Devil was apparently a victim of helpless bondage where she was concerned, and it is said that he once told her that he knew she would be the cause of his death, or of his going to the penitentiary for life. When he was not on the river he was often serving time on the "chain gang" for beating the woman, and the murder occurred just following his release from jail for this offense.

In Paducah, "Nine Hundred," especially the neighborhood of Biederman's Alley, is a questionable Negro section. It was here that Devil went in search of Vinie around midnight. It is said that he suspected the presence of a rival, but it was after a trivial argument over a cigarette that he sprang up from the bed on which he had been lying, and shrieking, "Fly high, you buzzard, but you'll have to light sometime," he lashed and thrust with his knife until his victim was unconscious. Even then, according to Negroes who witnessed the crime, he continued to strike in insane fury until he finally caught up a valise and fled.

A few days after Devil's trial and conviction he "got religion" in the county jail, and his weird chanting and frenzied shouting in his small cell throughout the following days and nights created a superstitious awe and terror among the other Negroes in the jail, as well as those gathered on the sidewalks outside. During Devil's last days, when he was not in a noisy religious ecstacy, he was giving advice and warning to the other prisoners, and "reading" religious books. To this illiterate and ignorant Negro a printed book could reveal nothing, but he would sit and turn the pages and gaze intently at the pictures.

Devil met his doom with a fair amount of composure. He watched the erection of the scaffold from his cell window, and remarked once, "I'm glad it's comin' nigh a close." His explanation of the crime was perhaps a sincere revelation of the poor creature's tortured abnormal nature. He insisted that he killed Vinie because he loved her.

The darkies were vividly impressed by the unfortunate and dramatic career of Devil Winston. Not only did this song commemorating his final crime become well known on the river and in the river towns, but Devil himself seems to have become vested in their minds with some of the qualities of the supernatural. At the present time the Negroes still speak of his death with a solemn belief that the professional services of the executioner were almost unequal to ridding the earth of this monster, and it is possible to hear strange tales of how the breath was finally pressed out of his body with flat irons, after the conventional methods of the State had failed to accomplish their purpose.

An old colored woman named Artie remembers the details of this unfortunate drama, and she gave me her impressions of the leading characters in it. Artie has been a faithful servant to three consecutive generations of her "white folks." One afternoon she had been washing curtains from the house of her present mistress, whom she speaks of, to close friends of the family, as "the chile." Artie was ready for an interlude from her work, and I was glad to find her in a talkative mood.

She put her hands on her hips and said, "Yes, honey, Devil wuz hung by law." She wanted me to understand the difference between "hangin' by law" and "jes' hangin'" or "mobbin'." She said, "Bless God, honey, when they's a-mobbin', the law don't have nothin' to do with it a-tall." Artie remembers that Devil was "a low, chunky nigger, with rusty skin an' kinky hair." Vinie, she recalls as "spare made" and light brown in color.

Devil's suspected rival continued to live quietly after the tragedy in the small town that had been so stirred by this violent crime. His life was apparently uneventful, and when he died a few years ago, a helpless feeble old Negro, no one would have ever associated him with any situation in which intense and unrestrained passion had played a part. For many years he had been known in the town as "Ole Stuttering Jim."

Artie said that Devil killed Vinie because "he wuz mean," and also because "he thought she had another man." Recalling the refrain of the song, I asked Artie if she thought Devil really did carry away a piece of Vinie's body in his grip. She replied, "Yes, Lawd, he sho' did. That nigger wuz jes' onery."

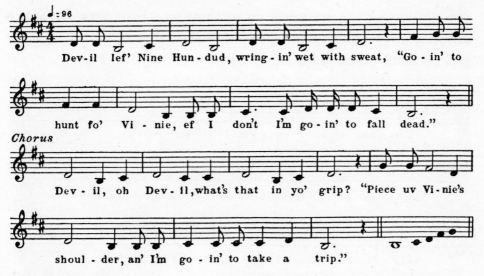

Dev-il lef' Nine Hun-dud, wring-in' wet with sweat, "Go-in' to
hunt fo' Vi-nie, ef I don't I'm go-in' to fall dead."

Chorus

Dev-il, oh Dev-il, what's that in yo' grip? "Piece uv Vi-nie's
shoul-der, an' I'm go-in' to take a trip."

Melody: Minor scale—4th and 7th omitted.

Devil lef' Nine Hundud, wringin' wet with sweat,
An' Devil killed po' Vinie, about a Duke cigarette.

Devil lef' Nine Hundud, the boys heered him say,
"I'm goin' to Biederman's Alley, to kill Vinie dead."

"Devil, oh Devil, see what you have done,
You have killed Vinie an' now you got to be hung."

When Devil walked on the gallus, he nevuh said a word,
"Now you've killed Vinie, an' you got to leave this worl'."

Late One Night

"Late One Night" was sung on the *Betsy Ann,* a favorite packet on the Ohio and Mississippi.

As we become familiar with these roustabout songs, we realize that in fairness we cannot judge the Negro of the "package boat" by standards the "white folks" have evolved for themselves. Especially while reading the songs of crime and lawlessness we could, in kindness and with wisdom, recall the lines of Joel Chandler Harris: "If the re-

sponsibilities of life are problems to those who have been trained to
solve them, how much more formidable must they be to this poor Negro, but lately lifted to his feet."[3]

Late one night I wuz mak-in' my roun', O-ver-took
my woman an' I blowed her down. I goes home an' goes to
bed, Place my pis-tol right in un-der my head.

Melody: First five tones of major scale.

Late in the night when I gits right,
I grab my pistol an' away I run.
I made a good run but I run too slow,
Got overtaken in a day or so.

Standin' on the corner readin' a bill,
Up walked a man named Thomas Hill,
"Say there, Bully, ain't yo' name Brown?
You look lak the man who shot his woman down."

I says, "Yes, my name is Lee Brown,
You have any writin', please read it to me."
"Consider yo'se'f under arrest,
Come on Bully, Jedge will tell you the rest."

When they arrested me I wuz dressed in black,
Put me in the train, they failed to carry me back.
Had no one to go my bail,
They place me way ovuh in Paris jail.

[3] "Mingo," published by Houghton Mifflin Company.

Early one mornin' 'bout half past nine,
I spied the Key-turner comin' down the line.
Knowed him by his walk, cleared his throat,
"Git ready, Bully, fo' this day's Co't."

'Bout five minutes befo' Co't begin,
Jedge charged the jury, twelve honest men.
'Bout five minutes aftuh Co't begin,
Jedge had my verdict in his right han'.

The verdict, murder in the first degree,
I cried, "Lawd, Lawd, have mercy on me."
I seen the Jedge pick up his pen,
Ninety-nine years in the ransom sea.[4]

Forty-fo' foot you're bound to go,
Down in the coal mine diggin' coal.
Forty-fo' foot, an' unduh the groun',
Pay for the day you shot yo' woman down.

You hear the people arguin' 'bout this song,
Some talk right and some talk wrong.
If anybody asks you who composed this song,
Po' long Jimmie been here and gone.

[4] This line was taken down as sung. Perhaps it should be "Ninety-nine years is the ransom, see?"

10

Appendix

NONE of the songs in the Appendix possesses characteristics not already discussed. Some are fragments of what were, no doubt, longer songs, and there are lines that are familiar to us from songs given in foregoing pages.

Because they can be heard today among the very old river Negroes, they are included in this collection. I hope that the writing of the words and melodies on paper will prevent them from disappearing altogether. Too many of their songs are already vanished, as these old roustabouts make the trip across the Deep River.

Beefsteak When I'm Hongry[1]

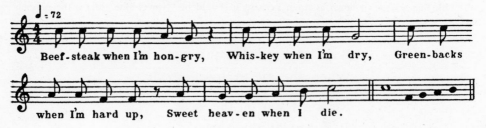

Melody: Five upper tones of major scale.

I went on down to Cairo,
Callin' fo' Sue,
Police got after me,
Tore my long tailed blue.

[1] Sung on the *Kentucky* and the *Joe Fowler.*

Sleigh bells is a-ringin',
Snow is a-fallin' fast,
Got my mule in the harness,
You got him hitched at last.

Green as greenbacks,
What do you 'sider me to be?
I'm a little boy frum the country,
You can't git away with me.

I offered the greenbacks,
I offered the change,
Last two lines missing.

Big Boat's Up the Rivuh

Big boat's up the riv - uh, An' she won't come down. I
b'lieve to my soul That she's wa - tuh boun'.

Melody: Pentatonic scale.

Captain done run
Evuh body up the hill.
Boys I'm a-goin' to quit her
When she git to Johnsonville.

Reason I stay on this boat
Such a great long time,
The woman I got
Treat me so nice an' kind.

Run up here, dog,
An' git yo' bone,
Show me what shoulder
You want it on.

I'm Goin' Down the Rivuh, Baby

I'm go-in' down the riv-uh Ba-by now I would car-ry you, I'm go-in' down the riv-uh Ba-by now I would car-ry you, Ain't noth-in' down the riv-uh That a bad look-in' wo-man kin do.

Melody: Major scale—4th omitted. The C♮ is an attempt to notate the characteristic slide.

When you see me leavin'
Hang black crepe ovuh yo' do',
When you see me leavin'
Hang black crepe ovuh yo' do'.
I'm leavin' this town,
An' I won't be back no mo'.

He'p me all you women,
That live in this town,
He'p me all you women,
That live in this town,

I'm too good a man,

Fo' you women to all let me down.

We will he'p you,

He'p you all we kin,

We will he'p you,

He'p you all we kin,

But the times is so hard,

Don't b'lieve we kin do you no good.

I'm Goin' to Ship on the Mike Davis[2]

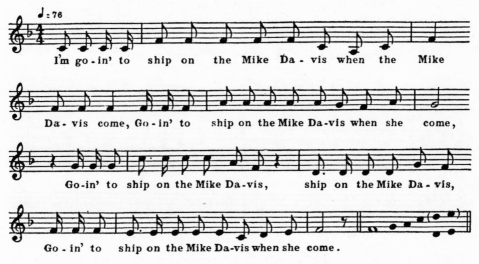

I'm go-in' to   ship on   the Mike Da-vis when the   Mike

Da-vis come, Go-in' to   ship on the Mike Da-vis when she   come,

Go-in' to ship on the Mike Da-vis,   ship on the Mike Da-vis,

Go-in' to   ship on the Mike Da-vis when she come.

Melody: Major scale—4th omitted.

Oh she landed at Golcondy when the Mike Davis come,

She landed at Golcondy when she come,

She landed at Golcondy, landed at Golcondy,

Oh she landed at Golcondy when she come.

*These lines are repeated with the names of Birdsville,
Metropolis, Cairo, Paducah, and other towns along the
river bank.*

[2] There is an evident connection between this melody and the tune of the mountaineer song, "She'll Be Comin' 'Round the Mountain." Both songs probably originated from the old Negro spiritual, "When the Chariot Comes." (See Carl Sandburg's *American Song Bag*, p. 372.)

The Kate Adams

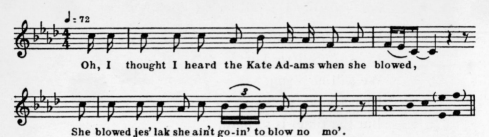

Melody: Pentatonic scale.

The reason that I lak the Kate Adams so,
She carries a chambermaid an' a watch below.

Come on boys with yo' neck out long,
Show me what shoulder you want it on.

The Macombrey Queen

Melody: Major scale with the 7th lowered.
Phrase groups of three.

So I got to git ready,
We're goin' to New Orleans,
So I got to git ready,
We're goin' to New Orleans,
On the purtiest steamboat,
It's the Macombrey Queen.

Courtesy of W. L. Beasley, Jr.

LIVINGSTON POINT

WHERE THE OHIO AND THE TENNESSEE RIVERS MEET

My Man's Up the Rivuh

My man's up the riv-uh, An' I tole him not to go,
That he would be both-ered With the frost an' snow. All the go,
Chorus
all the go, Me an' my yel-low gals all the go.

Melody: Pentatonic scale.

An' ef you don't lak me
You kin let me go,
I'll git on the James Lee
An' go below.[3]

On the Banks uv the Ole Tennessee

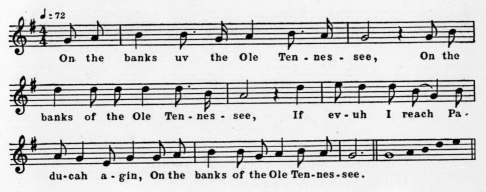

On the banks uv the Ole Ten-nes-see, On the
banks of the Ole Ten-nes-see, If ev-uh I reach Pa-
du-cah a-gin, On the banks of the Ole Ten-nes-see.

Melody: Pentatonic scale.

[3] To "go below" meant to go down into the cotton country—Memphis, Vicksburg, New Orleans.

The Po' Ole Slave

The po' ole slave is dead an' gone, We know that he is free. Dis - turb him not, but let him rest A - way down in Ten - nes - see.

Melody: First six tones of major scale.

The po' ole slave is gone to rest,
No master does he fear,
 Disturb him not, but let him rest,
Away down in Tennessee.

Woman, Woman, I Seen Yo' Man

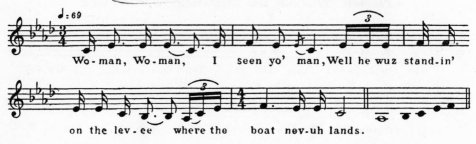

Wo - man, Wo - man, I seen yo' man, Well he wuz stand - in' on the lev - ee where the boat nev - uh lands.

Melody: Pentatonic scale.

Captain, captain, have the money come?
It'll be here today or tomorry one.

Captain George he ride a big bay hoss,
He's a mighty fine man, but he don't pay off.

Nevuh mind, I'll see you agin,
I'll see you when yo' head's hangin' jes' lak mine.

You Talk About Yo' Greenbacks

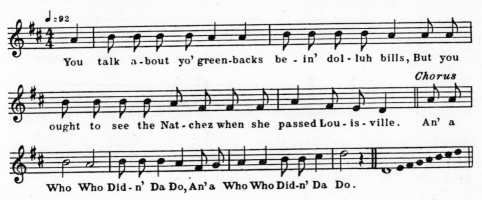

You talk a-bout yo' green-backs be-in' dol-luh bills, But you
ought to see the Nat-chez when she passed Lou-is-ville. An' a
Chorus
Who Who Did-n' Da Do, An' a Who Who Did-n' Da Do.

Melody: Major scale.

Said he had a little gal dressed in red,
Goin' to make a livin' with a needle an' thread.

Had a little gal dressed in blue,
Goin' to make a livin' good an' true.

Yonder comes a boat shootin' through the fog,
Lice on her annoy you like a hog.

Oh lan' this boat, an' I'll jump asho',
Goodbye Sally, nevuh see you no mo'.

Index of Songs

Ain't Got No Place to Lay My Head 80

Alberta, Let Yo' Hair Hang Low 85

Beefsteak When I'm Hongry 112

Been All Aroun' the Whole Roun' Worl' 103

Big Boat's Up the Rivuh 113

B'y' Sara Burned Down 40

Captain Jim Rees an' the Katie 10

Careless Love 89

Carryin' Sacks 29

Come, Love, Come, the Boat Lies Low 90

Come On, My Pink, an' Tell Me What You Think 87

Devil 105

Down the Rivuh, Down, Boys 38

Duke See the Tie Pile 23

Early in the Mornin' 104

Ferd Herold Blues 53

Gabriel's Trumpet 71

God Dawg My Lousy Soul 25

Gold Dust Fire, The 41

Golden City 51

I Am Waitin' on the Levee 57

I Come Up Out uv Egypt 68

Ida Red 14

I'm Alabama Bound 54

I'm Goin' Down the Rivuh 50

I'm Goin' Down the Rivuh, Baby 114

I'm Goin' Down the Rivuh Befo' Long 29

I'm Goin' to Ship on the Mike Davis 115

I'm Goin' Up the Rivuh 31

I'm the Man That Kin Raise So Long 27

I'm Wukin' My Way Back Home 13

Is Yo' Lamps Gone Out? 75
I Wuz Borned on the Rivuh 32
Jesus Nevuh Come in the Mornin' 72
Joe Fowler Blues, The 46
John Gilbert 43
Kate Adams, The 116
Katie an' the Jim Lee Had a Little Race 18
Katie an' the Jim Lee Had a Race 55
Late One Night 109
Macombrey Queen, The 116
Master Had a Bran' New Coat 24
My Man's Up the Rivuh 117
Oh, Annie, Oh! 35
Ohio Rivuh, She's So Deep an' Wide 81
Oh, When I Git My New House Done 15
On the Banks uv the Ole Tennessee 117
Po' Ole Slave, The 118
Po' Shine 17
Red Sea 70
Rowdy Soul 93
She Leaves Memphis 20
Skinner, Skinner, You Know the Rule 23
Soundings (The Song of the Leadsman) 61-66
Stacker Lee, No. 1 100
Stacker Lee, No. 2 100
Stacker Lee, No. 3 102
Stavin Chain 16
Take Yo' Time 97
This Ole Worl' Ain't Goin' to Stan' Much Longer 73
Uncle Bud 94
Uphead an' Scatter, Boys 83
Vicksburg 'Round the Bend 22
Where Wuz You Las' Night? 77
Woman, Woman, I Seen Yo' Man 118
You Talk About Yo' Greenbacks 119